DIRT POOR VS PAY DIRT

The Allergy Book

Chase Duquesnay & EnQi ReaL

Amazon

Parents

I believe the children are our future...

- DOPEST COLLAB EVER

CONTENTS

CONTENTS

AUBREE

This book we wrote primarily for Aubree, she was highly upset that they asked her to stop bringing Peanut Butter Sandwiches to school!

We had to have a long discussion about Allergies that took us all the way back in time and then into the future.

NATURE VS NURTURE

Up front References...

Manetho is thought to have recorded the work of an early anatomist. In his work History of Egypt, **Manetho states the pharaoh Djer was an anatomist.** Djer (or Zer or Sekhty)[1] is considered the third pharaoh of the First Dynasty of ancient Egypt in current Egyptology.

Knowledge of anatomical studies is drawn from papyri and ostraca, especially the Ebers, Edwin Smith and Kahun Papyri. One of only two extant texts on creating a mummy is the Ritual of Embalming Papyrus. Mummification techniques led to advancement in anatomical knowledge.

Dated to circa 1800 BCE, the Kahun Gynaecological Papyrus is the oldest known medical text in Egypt. The Ramesseum medical papyri consist of 17 individual papyri that were found in the great temple of the Ramesseum. The Papyri was buried under a brick magazine discovered by Flinders Petrie and James Quibell in 1895.[11] They concentrate on the eyes, gynecology, paediatrics, muscles and tendons. Dated to circa 1600 BCE, the Edwin Smith Papyrus is the only surviving copy of part of an ancient Egyptian textbook on trauma surgery.

The Ebers Papyrus was also purchased by Edwin Smith in 1862. The papyrus dates to around 1550BC and covers 110 pages, making it the lengthiest of the medical papyri. The papyrus covers many different topics including; dermatology, digestive diseases, traumatic diseases, dentistry and gynecological conditions.

The earliest known report of an allergy was that of King Menses of Egypt, who died after a wasp sting some time between 3640 and 3300 BC. Shen Nong (c. 2700 BC) is considered the Father of Chinese Herbal Medicine. According to legend, he was the first to taste ephedra which was used to treat asthma-like symptoms five thousand years ago.

Ephedra, known to the inhabitants of China as Ma Huang, was used to relieve bronchospasms, produce vasoconstriction, reverse congestion, and inhibit mucus secretion.

The Nei Ching Su Wen, or the "Cannon of Internal Medicine," which is (arguably) the world's oldest treatise of internal medicine, describes respiratory distress which may refer to what we now consider asthma:

"Man is afflicted when he cannot rest and when his breathing has a sound (is noisy) or when he cannot rest and his breathing is without any sound. He may rise and rest (his habits of life may be) as of old and his breathing is noisy; he may have his rest and his exercise and his breathing is troubled (wheezing, panting): or he may not get any rest and be unable to walk about and his breathing is troubled. There are those who do not get a rest and those who rest and yet have troubled breathing."

The Ebers papyrus was unearthed in Thebes in 1862 and then translated into German in 1873! In the Ebers Papyrus, asthma was considered to be a whdw, a "disorder or foulness," of the metu, ducts that were thought to distribute air and water to the organs, including the lungs. Physicians, therefore, attempted to heal the ducts by dispelling the "foulness." (They made the first ventilators or asthma pump depending on how you view the technology)...

"Thou shalt fetch seven stones and heat them by fire, thou shalt take one thereof and place a little of these remedies on it and cover it with a new vessel whose bottom is perforated, and place a stalk of reed in this hole; thou shalt put thy mouth to this stalk so that thou inhalest the smoke of it. Likewise with all stones."

The Ebers Papyrus is dated to about 1552 B.C.E. (WHI 2008), 1534 B.C.E. (Demand 2000), or 1536 (Carpenter et al. 1998), based on the passage on the verso referring to the ninth year of the reign of Amenhotep I (Demand 2000). However, there is a portion of the papyrus (paragraph 856a) that suggests a considerable earlier origin—a reference to the Lower Egypt Den that would place an origin nearer to the First Dynasty (about 3000 B.C.E.).

The Hearst Papyrus was offered in 1901 to the Hearst Expedition in Egypt. It concentrated on treatments for problems dealing with the urinary system, blood, hair, and bites.

The London Medical Papyrus is located in the British Museum and dates back to Tutankhamun. The focus of the London Medical Papyrus is holistically spiritual and relies heavily on spells that deal with the supernatural.

*Here I need to interject and add Microscopic Pathogens were known in ancient times as demons etc... What other cultures later attribute to "magic" or superstition is largely misunderstood science, with a lil sauce on it LOL...

The Carlsberg Papyrus sheds light on how women will conceive and whether or not they will conceive, using garlic. This garlic is used as an indicator once properly placed in the body of a woman. The Chester Beatty Medical Papyrus is named after Sir Alfred Chester Beatty who donated 19 papyri to the British Museum. The remedies in these texts are generally related to magic and focus on conditions that involve headaches and anorectal ailments. The Brooklyn Papyrus – Focusing mainly on snakebites, the Brooklyn Papyrus speaks of remedial methods for poisons obtained from snakes, scorpions, and tarantulas. The Brooklyn Papyrus currently resides in the Brooklyn Museum. - Wiki

Proof the Ancient Egyptians were primarily Vegan/Vegetarian!!!

Diet of ancient Egyptians inferred from stable isotope systematics

Author links open overlay panel
Alexandra Touzeau a, Romain Amiot a, Janne Blichert-Toft b, Jean-Pierre Flandrois c, François Fourel a, Vincent Grossi a, François Martineau a, Pascale Richardin d, Christophe Lécuyer a
Show more
Add to Mendeley
Share
Cite
https://doi.org/10.1016/j.jas.2014.03.005
Get rights and content

Highlights

- .   .

    Carbonate $\delta13C$ was measured in tooth enamel and bone of Ancient Egyptians.

- δ13C remains largely constant from 5500 to 2000 BP and indicates very low C4-intake.

- High δ15N of mummy hair is indicative of aridity and not of trophic level.

- δ13C of hair indicates <50% of dietary protein came from animals.

- Sulfur isotopes suggest that fish, such as the Nile Perch, was not regularly consumed.

Abstract

Carbon, nitrogen and sulfur stable isotope compositions were measured in hard and soft tissues from Egyptian mummies of humans and animals in order to track the diet of ancient Egyptians from 5500 to 1500 years B.P. The carbon isotope ratios of bone apatite (δ13Cbo = -14.3 ± 0.9‰) and hair protein (δ13Ch = -19.9‰) <u>**are compatible with a diet based almost exclusively on C3-derived food**</u> (proportion of C4 < 10%). Less negative carbon isotope ratios of enamel (δ13Cen = -11.6 ±0.7‰) relative to bones from the same mummies could be the result of differences in the chemical microenvironment in which mineralization occurred, as well as of differences in diet between children and adults, in particular through the consumption of milk or millet gruel during infancy and childhood. High values of nitrogen isotope ratios for hair protein (δ15Nh = 9.1‰–15.5‰) are ascribed to aridity rather than fish consumption because the δ34S values of human hair are lower than those measured in Nile perch scales. Except for Coptic mummies, the constancy of δ13Cbo and δ13Cen over a duration of ~3000 years is striking considering the various political, technological, and cultural changes that impacted the Egyptian civilization during this time interval.

Introduction

Ancient Egypt stands out as one of the first great civilizations that emerged at the end of the Neolithic period (6000 B.P.) and is particularly renowned for its exceptional longevity. Throughout its long history, ancient Egypt alternated between periods of stability and prosperity, and troubled times resulting from episodes of war or severe drought. The central government was overthrown and restored several times, and the shape of the Egyptian territory itself was modified through military conquests or defeats. Not all of these political events directly influenced the day-to-day life of the population, but they facilitated innovation through adaptation or assimilation of foreign customs and technologies, resulting in cultural and economic evolution over the centuries. This intrinsic evolution of ancient Egypt is expected to have had consequences such as major changes in life expectancy and culinary habits. The diet of ancient Egyptians reflects how they were utilizing natural resources, whether through trade or living only on what they themselves could produce, with both strategies having different outcomes for their environment. For example, food and timber trade between ancient Egypt and distant countries (Gardiner, 1961, Trigger et al., 1983) is known well before the establishment of the spice and silk routes between Europe and South-East Asia during the Middle Ages. Variation in diet also testifies to progressive agricultural practices through the development of new tools and irrigation techniques such as the shaduf, which appeared during the New Kingdom (3300 B.P.; Butzer, 1976).

Current knowledge of the diet of ancient Egyptians arises from two major sources of information. Figurative depictions exhibit the food products that were known to ancient Egyptians and also reveal how they were processing cereals and fruits into bread, beer, and wine (Alcock, 2006). These portrayals are, however, often biased because they mostly represent the food consumed by higher social classes, who could afford paying artists to commit costly festive meals to perpetuity. They are further difficult to interpret because translation of names of ingredients often is ambiguous and probably not exhaustive. Food and cooking recipes also can be deduced from the analysis of food remains preserved in either graves or middens (David, 2007, Samuel, 2000, van Neer et al., 2004) or at habitation sites (Bagnall, 2006, Redding, 1984, Smith, 2003, Wetterstrom, 1984). Beyond the identification of food products, their average proportion in the daily diet of ancient Egyptians is a key parameter remaining difficult to estimate. Large consumption of gritted bread is certain because of the notable common dental wear in human remains (Gamza and Irish, 2012, Leek, 1972). As for other food sources such as vegetables, fish or meat, only indirect inferences can be made by considering the salaries paid in kind to pyramid workers and craftsmen from the King's valley. These indicate that ancient Egyptians consumed large amounts of cereals through bread and beer, and also ate vegetables (e.g. onions, lettuce) and legumes (e.g. peas, fenugreek, lentils). Meat is not mentioned and probably represented a very small portion of the diet, except for the wealthiest people. For the working classes, animal proteins were rare and came from dairy foods, fowl, and fish.

The stable isotope analysis of human tissues can provide complementary information on the diet of ancient Egyptians, with the possibility of estimating the relative proportions of plants and animal proteins of terrestrial or aquatic origin. With this purpose in mind we measured the carbon isotope compositions of human bone apatite ($\delta13Cbo$), enamel apatite ($\delta13Cen$) and hair ($\delta13Ch$) in order to quantify the relative proportions of C3- and C4-derived foods in the diet of ancient Egyptians and how this diet evolved from the Predynastic Period (~ 5500 B.P.) to Byzantine Egypt (~ 1500 B.P.). Along with the carbon, nitrogen and sulfur isotope compositions of soft tissues (feathers, scales, and hair) of various animal samples (fish, birds, and mammals), we also analyzed $\delta34Sh$ and $\delta15Nh$ of human hair samples to evaluate how animal protein and freshwater food may have contributed to the diet of ancient Egyptians.

Section snippets

Stable isotope ratios and their potential for recording dietary patterns

The use of 13C/12C ratios in diet reconstruction is based on the distinction between different pathways of carbon fixation in plants (Bender, 1971, O'Leary, 1988, Smith and Epstein, 1971). The C3-plant group is by far the most diverse and comprises the majority of vegetables, cereals, and fruits, while C4-plants are rare, and limited to millet and sorghum in Africa. C3-plants strongly discriminate against 13C during photosynthesis, and these plants therefore are markedly depleted in 13C

Material and analytical methods

Samples of human hair, enamel, and bone were collected from Egyptian mummified heads and Predynastic individuals kept in the Musée des Confluences, Lyon, France, as well as from Coptic mummies preserved in the Musée Testut-Latarjet d'Anatomie, Lyon, France. The mummies originate from different localities in the Egyptian Nile Valley (Table 1;

Fig. 1). The age and sex of the mummies are unknown. However the collection of dynastic heads was previously studied by Herzberg and Perrot (1983) who

Results

The carbon isotope ratios measured in bone apatite ($\delta 13Cbo$) and enamel ($\delta 13Cen$) samples from the present study are listed in Table 1 and plotted in Fig. 2. The average bone $\delta 13Cbo$ value is -14.3 ± 0.9‰, which is identical within the quoted errors to Iacumin et al.'s (1996) value of -14.4 ± 0.5‰. The average enamel $\delta 13Cen$ value is -11.6 ± 0.6‰, again identical within the quoted errors to the average value of -11.8 ± 1.1‰ at Tombos, Nubia (Buzon and Bowen, 2010), and comparable to the average

Preservation of tissue stable isotope compositions

The most common diagenetic processes that can alter the carbon isotope compositions of bone and enamel are the chemical and isotopic exchanges of carbonate ions with groundwater and soil water after burial and the dissolution and recrystallization of mineralized tissues (Wright and Schwarcz, 1996). These processes are particularly enhanced in the presence of fluids and under microbially-mediated conditions (Zazzo et al., 2004). The dry conditions prevailing in Egypt therefore minimize the risk

Conclusions

Carbon isotope ratios were measured in enamel, bone, and hair of ancient Egyptians. A significant offset ($+2.5$‰) is observed between the $\delta 13C$ values of teeth and bones that cannot be ascribed to the weaning effect. Following Warinner and Tuross (2009), this isotopic offset rather may be caused by differences in mineralization conditions of the two types of tissue. Using tissue-specific equations, the $\delta 13C$ value of the reconstructed diet is comparable and close to the average value of C3-plants

Over 85 percent of plant species are called C3 because the enzyme Rubisco converts the carbon dioxide into a **carbohydrate** made up of three carbon atoms. C3 (3 carbon product of **green plant** photosynthesis) plants include: algae, rice, wheat, soybeans, hibiscus, lemons, lotus, mango, peas, radishes, tomatoes, wheat, jackfruit, guava, onion, potatoes, oats, peppers, coconuts, grapes, peanuts, plums, beets, sunflower, palm

(Batana), watermelons etc...

Pharmaceuticals

The pharmaceutical industry is an industry in medicine that discovers, develops, produces, and markets pharmaceutical drugs for use as medications to be administered to patients (or self-administered), with the aim to cure and prevent diseases, or alleviate symptoms.[1][2] Pharmaceutical companies may deal in generic or brand medications and medical devices. They are subject to a variety of laws and regulations that govern the patenting, testing, safety, efficacy using drug testing and marketing of drugs. The global pharmaceuticals market produced treatments worth $1,228.45 billion in 2020 and showed a compound annual growth rate (CAGR) of 1.8%.[3]

History[edit]

Main article: History of pharmacy

Mid-1800s – 1945: From botanicals to the first synthetic drugs[edit]

The modern era of pharmaceutical industry began with local apothecaries that expanded from their traditional role of distributing botanical drugs such as morphine and quinine to wholesale manufacture in the mid-1800s, and from discoveries resulting from applied research. Intentional drug discovery from plants began with the isolation between 1803 and 1805 of morphine – an analgesic and sleep-inducing agent – from opium by the German apothecary assistant Friedrich Sertürner, who named this compound after the Greek god of dreams, Morpheus.[4] By the late 1880s, German dye manufacturers had perfected the purification of individual organic compounds from tar and other mineral sources and had also established rudimentary methods in organic chemical synthesis.[5] The development of synthetic chemical methods allowed scientists to systematically vary the structure of chemical substances, and growth in the emerging science of pharmacology expanded their ability to evaluate the biological effects of these structural changes.

Epinephrine, norepinephrine, and amphetamine[edit]

By the 1890s, the profound effect of adrenal extracts on many different tissue types had been discovered, setting off a search both for the mechanism of chemical signalling and efforts to exploit these observations for the development of new drugs. The blood pressure raising and vasoconstrictive effects of adrenal extracts were of particular interest to surgeons as hemostatic agents and as treatment for shock, and a number of companies developed products based on adrenal extracts containing varying purities of the active substance. In 1897, John Abel of Johns Hopkins University identified the active principle as epinephrine, which he isolated in an impure state as the sulfate salt. Industrial chemist Jōkichi Takamine later developed a method for obtaining epinephrine in a pure state, and licensed the technology to Parke-Davis. Parke-Davis marketed epinephrine under the trade name Adrenalin. Injected epinephrine proved to be especially efficacious for the acute treatment of asthma attacks, and an inhaled version was sold in the United States until 2011 (Primatene Mist).[6][7] By 1929 epinephrine had been formulated into an inhaler for use in the treatment of nasal congestion.

While highly effective, the requirement for injection limited the use of epinephrine[clarification needed] and orally active derivatives were sought. A structurally similar compound, ephedrine, was identified by Japanese chemists in the Ma Huang plant and marketed by Eli Lilly as an oral treatment for asthma. Following the work of Henry Dale and George Barger at Burroughs-Wellcome, academic chemist Gordon Alles synthesized amphetamine and tested it in asthma patients in 1929. The drug proved to have only modest anti-asthma effects but produced sensations of exhilaration and palpitations. Amphetamine was developed by Smith, Kline and French as a nasal decongestant under the trade name Benzedrine Inhaler. Amphetamine was eventually developed for the treatment of narcolepsy, post-encephalitic parkinsonism, and mood elevation in depression and other psychiatric indications. It received approval as a New and Nonofficial Remedy from the American Medical Association for these uses in 1937,[8] and remained in common use for depression until the development of tricyclic antidepressants in the 1960s.[7]

Discovery and development of the barbiturates[edit]

Diethylbarbituric acid was the first marketed barbiturate. It was sold by Bayer under the trade name Veronal.

In 1903, Hermann Emil Fischer and Joseph von Mering disclosed their discovery that diethylbarbituric acid, formed from the reaction of diethylmalonic acid, phosphorus oxychloride and urea, induces sleep in dogs. The discovery was patented and licensed to Bayer pharmaceuticals, which marketed the compound under the trade name Veronal as a sleep aid beginning in 1904. Systematic investigations of the effect of structural changes on potency and duration of action led to the discovery of phenobarbital at Bayer in 1911 and the discovery of its potent anti-epileptic activity in 1912. Phenobarbital was among the most widely used drugs for the treatment of epilepsy through the 1970s, and as of 2014, remains on the World Health Organizations list of essential medications.[9][10] The 1950s and 1960s saw increased awareness of the addictive properties and abuse potential of barbiturates and amphetamines and led to increasing restrictions on their use and growing government oversight of prescribers. Today, amphetamine is largely restricted to use in the treatment of attention deficit disorder and phenobarbital in the treatment of epilepsy. [11][12]

In 1958, Leo Sternbach discovered the first benzodiazepine, chlordiazepoxide (Librium). Dozens of other benzodiazepines have been developed and are in use, some of the more popular drugs being diazepam (Valium), alprazolam (Xanax), clonazepam (Klonopin), and lorazepam (Ativan). Due to their far superior safety and therapeutic properties, benzodiazepines have largely replaced the use of barbiturates in medicine, except in certain special cases. When it was later discovered that benzodiazepines, like barbiturates, significantly lose their effectiveness and can have serious side effects when taken long-term, Heather Ashton researched benzodiazepine dependence and developed a protocol to discontinue their use.

Insulin[edit]

A series of experiments performed from the late 1800s to the early 1900s revealed that diabetes is caused by the absence of a substance normally produced by the pancreas. In 1869, Oskar Minkowski and Joseph von Mering found that diabetes could be induced in dogs by surgical removal of the pancreas. In 1921, Canadian professor Frederick Banting and his student Charles Best repeated this study and found that injections of pancreatic extract reversed the symptoms produced by pancreas removal. Soon, the extract was demonstrated to work in people, but development of insulin therapy as a routine medical procedure was delayed by difficulties in producing the material in sufficient quantity and with reproducible purity. The researchers sought assistance from industrial collaborators at Eli Lilly and Co. based on the company's experience with large scale purification of biological materials. Chemist **George B. Walden** of Eli Lilly and Company found that careful adjustment of the pH of the extract allowed a relatively pure grade of insulin to be produced. Under pressure from Toronto University and a potential patent challenge by academic scientists who had independently developed a similar purification method, an agreement was reached for non-exclusive production of insulin by multiple companies. Prior to the discovery and widespread availability of insulin therapy the life expectancy of diabetics was only a few months.[13]

Early anti-infective research: Salvarsan, Prontosil, Penicillin and vaccines[edit]

The development of drugs for the treatment of infectious diseases was a major focus of early research and development efforts; in 1900, pneumonia, tuberculosis, and diarrhea were the three leading causes of death in the United States and mortality in the first year of life exceeded 10%.[14][15][failed verification]

In 1911 arsphenamine, the first synthetic anti-infective drug, was developed by Paul Ehrlich and chemist **Alfred Bertheim** of the Institute of Experimental Therapy in Berlin. The drug was given the commercial name Salvarsan.[16] Ehrlich, noting both the general toxicity of arsenic and the selective absorption of certain dyes by bacteria, hypothesized that an arsenic-containing dye with similar selective absorption properties could be used to treat bacterial infections. Arsphenamine was prepared as part of a campaign to synthesize a series of such compounds, and was found to exhibit partially selective toxicity. Arsphenamine proved to be the first effective treatment for syphilis, a disease untl then had been incurable and led inexorably to severe skin ulceration, neurological damage, and death.[17]

Ehrlich's approach of systematically varying the chemical structure of synthetic compounds and measuring the effects of these changes on biological activity was pursued broadly by industrial scientists, including **Bayer** scientists Josef Klarer, Fritz Mietzsch, and **Gerhard Domagk**. This work, also based on the testing of compounds available from the German dye industry, led to the development of Prontosil, the first representative of the sulfonamide class of antibiotics. Compared to arsphenamine, the sulfonamides had a broader spectrum of activity and were far less toxic, rendering them useful for infections caused by pathogens such as **streptococci**.[18] In 1939, Domagk received the Nobel Prize in Medicine for this discovery.[19][20] Nonetheless, the dramatic decrease in deaths from infectious diseases that occurred prior to World War II was primarily the result of improved public health measures such as clean water and less crowded housing, and the impact of anti-infective drugs and vaccines was significant mainly after World War II.[21][22]

In 1928, Alexander Fleming discovered the antibacterial effects of penicillin, but its exploitation for the treatment of human disease awaited the development of methods for its large scale production and purification. These were developed by a U.S. and British government-led consortium of pharmaceutical companies during the world war.[23]

There was early progress toward the development of vaccines throughout this period, primarily in the form of academic and government-funded basic research directed toward the identification of the pathogens responsible for common communicable diseases. In 1885, Louis Pasteur and Pierre Paul Émile Roux created the first rabies vaccine. The first diphtheria vaccines were produced in 1914 from a mixture of diphtheria toxin and antitoxin (produced from the serum of an inoculated animal), but the safety of the inoculation was marginal and it was not widely used. The United States recorded 206,000 cases of diphtheria in 1921, resulting in 15,520 deaths. In 1923, parallel efforts by Gaston Ramon at the Pasteur Institute and Alexander Glenny at the Wellcome Research Laboratories (later part of GlaxoSmithKline) led to the discovery that a safer vaccine could be produced by treating diphtheria toxin with formaldehyde.[24] In 1944, Maurice Hilleman of Squibb Pharmaceuticals developed the first vaccine against Japanese Encephalitis.[25] Hilleman later moved to Merck, where he played a key role in the development of vaccines against measles, mumps, chickenpox, rubella, hepatitis A, hepatitis B, and meningitis.

Unsafe drugs and early industry regulation[edit]

In 1937 over 100 people died after ingesting a solution of the antibacterial sulfanilamide formulated in the toxic solvent diethylene glycol.

Prior to the 20th century, drugs were generally produced by small scale manufacturers with little regulatory control over manufacturing or claims of safety and efficacy. To the extent that such laws did exist, enforcement was lax. In the United States, increased regulation of vaccines and other biological drugs was spurred by tetanus outbreaks and deaths caused by the distribution of contaminated smallpox vaccine and diphtheria antitoxin.[26] The Biologics Control Act of 1902 required that federal government grant premarket approval for every biological drug and for the process and facility producing such drugs. This was followed in 1906 by the Pure Food and Drugs Act, which forbade the interstate distribution of adulterated or misbranded foods and drugs. A drug was considered misbranded if it contained alcohol, morphine, opium, cocaine, or any of several other potentially dangerous or addictive drugs, and if its label failed to indicate the quantity or proportion of such drugs. The government's attempts to use the law to prosecute manufacturers for making unsupported claims of efficacy were undercut by a Supreme Court ruling restricting the federal government's enforcement powers to cases of incorrect specification of the drug's ingredients.[27]

In 1937 over 100 people died after ingesting "Elixir Sulfanilamide" manufactured by S.E. Massengill Company of Tennessee. The product was formulated in diethylene glycol, a highly toxic solvent that is now widely used as antifreeze.[28] Under the laws extant at that time, prosecution of the manufacturer was possible only under the technicality that the product had been called an "elixir", which literally implied a solution in ethanol. In response to this episode, the U.S. Congress passed the Federal Food, Drug, and Cosmetic Act of 1938, which for the first time required pre-market demonstration of safety before a drug could be sold, and explicitly prohibited false therapeutic claims.[29]

The post-war years, 1945–1970[edit]

Further advances in anti-infective research[edit]

The aftermath of World War II saw an explosion in the discovery of new classes of antibacterial drugs[30] including the cephalosporins (developed by Eli Lilly based on the seminal work of Giuseppe Brotzu and Edward Abraham),[31] [32] streptomycin (discovered during a Merck-funded research program in Selman Waksman's laboratory[33]), the tetracyclines[34] (discovered at Lederle Laboratories, now a part of Pfizer), erythromycin (discovered at Eli Lilly and Co.)[35] and their extension to an increasingly wide range of bacterial pathogens. Streptomycin, discovered during a Merck-funded research program in Selman Waksman's laboratory at Rutgers in 1943, became the first effective treatment for tuberculosis. At the time of its discovery, sanitoriums for the isolation of tuberculosis-infected people were an ubiquitous feature of cities in developed countries, with 50% dying within 5 years of admission.[33][36]

A Federal Trade Commission report issued in 1958 attempted to quantify the effect of antibiotic development on American public health. The report found that over the period 1946–1955, there was a 42% drop in the incidence of diseases for which antibiotics were effective and only a 20% drop in those for which antibiotics were not effective. The report concluded that "it appears that the use of antibiotics, early diagnosis, and other factors have limited the epidemic spread and thus the number of these diseases which have occurred". The study further examined mortality rates for eight common diseases for which antibiotics offered effective therapy (syphilis, tuberculosis, dysentery, scarlet fever, whooping cough, meningococcal infections, and pneumonia), and found a 56% decline over the same period.[37] Notable among these was a 75% decline in deaths due to tuberculosis.[38]

Measles cases reported in the United States before and after introduction of the vaccine

Percent surviving by age in 1900, 1950, and 1997[39]

During the years 1940–1955, the rate of decline in the U.S. death rate accelerated from 2% per year to 8% per year, then returned to the historical rate of 2% per year. The dramatic decline in the immediate post-war years has been attributed to the rapid development of new treatments and vaccines for infectious disease that occurred during these years.[40][22] Vaccine development continued to accelerate, with the most notable achievement of the period being Jonas Salk's 1954 development of the polio vaccine under the funding of the non-profit National Foundation for Infantile Paralysis. The vaccine process was never patented but was instead given to pharmaceutical companies to manufacture as a low-cost generic. In 1960 Maurice Hilleman of Merck Sharp & Dohme identified the SV40 virus, which was later shown to cause tumors in many mammalian species. It was later determined that SV40 was present as a contaminant in polio vaccine lots that had been administered to 90% of the children in the United States.[41][42] The contamination appears to have originated both in the original cell stock and in monkey tissue used for production. In 2004 the National Cancer Institute announced that it had concluded that SV40 is not associated with cancer in people.[43]

Other notable new vaccines of the period include those for measles (1962, John Franklin Enders of Children's Medical Center Boston, later refined by Maurice Hilleman at Merck), Rubella (1969, Hilleman, Merck) and mumps (1967, Hilleman, Merck)[44] The United States incidences of rubella, congenital rubella syndrome, measles, and mumps all fell by >95% in the immediate aftermath of widespread vaccination.[45] The first 20 years of licensed measles vaccination in the U.S. prevented an estimated 52 million cases of the disease, 17,400 cases of mental retardation, and 5,200 deaths.[46]

Development and marketing of antihypertensive drugs[edit]

Hypertension is a risk factor for atherosclerosis,[47] heart failure,[48] coronary artery disease,[49][50] stroke,[51] renal disease,[52][53] and peripheral arterial disease,[54][55] and is the most important risk factor for cardiovascular morbidity and mortality, in industrialized countries.[56] Prior to 1940 approximately 23% of all deaths among persons over age 50 were attributed to hypertension. Severe cases of hypertension were treated by surgery.[57]

Early developments in the field of treating hypertension included quaternary ammonium ion sympathetic nervous system blocking agents, but these compounds were never widely used due to their severe side effects, because the long-term health consequences of high blood pressure had not yet been established, and because they had to be administered by injection.

In 1952 researchers at Ciba discovered the first orally available vasodilator, hydralazine.[58] A major shortcoming of hydralazine monotherapy was that it lost its effectiveness over time (tachyphylaxis). In the mid-1950s Karl H. Beyer, James M. Sprague, John E. Baer, and Frederick C. Novello of Merck and Co. discovered and developed chlorothiazide, which remains the most widely used antihypertensive drug today.[59] This development was associated with a substantial decline in the mortality rate among people with hypertension.[60] The inventors were recognized by a Public Health Lasker Award in 1975 for "the saving of untold thousands of lives and the alleviation of the suffering of millions of victims of hypertension".[61]

A 2009 Cochrane review concluded that thiazide antihypertensive drugs reduce the risk of death (RR 0.89), stroke (RR 0.63), coronary heart disease (RR 0.84), and cardiovascular events (RR 0.70) in people with high blood pressure.[62] In the ensuring years other classes of antihypertensive drug were developed and found wide acceptance in combination therapy, including loop diuretics (Lasix/furosemide, Hoechst Pharmaceuticals, 1963),[63] beta blockers (ICI Pharmaceuticals, 1964)[64] ACE inhibitors, and angiotensin receptor blockers. ACE inhibitors reduce the risk of new onset kidney disease [RR 0.71] and death [RR 0.84] in diabetic patients, irrespective of whether they have hypertension.[65]

Oral Contraceptives[edit]

Prior to the Second World war, birth control was prohibited in many countries, and in the United States even the discussion of contraceptive methods sometimes led to prosecution under Comstock laws. The history of the development of oral contraceptives is thus closely tied to the birth control movement and the efforts of activists Margaret Sanger, Mary Dennett, and Emma Goldman. Based on fundamental research performed by Gregory Pincus and synthetic methods for progesterone developed by Carl Djerassi at Syntex and by Frank Colton at G.D. Searle & Co., the first oral contraceptive, Enovid, was developed by G.D. Searle & Co. and approved by the FDA in 1960. The original formulation incorporated vastly excessive doses of hormones, and caused severe side effects. Nonetheless, by 1962, 1.2 million American women were on the pill, and by 1965 the number had increased to 6.5 million.[66][67][68][69] The availability of a convenient form of temporary contraceptive led to dramatic changes in social mores including expanding the range of lifestyle options available to women, reducing the reliance of women on men for contraceptive practice, encouraging the delay of marriage, and increasing pre-marital co-habitation.[70]

Thalidomide and the Kefauver-Harris Amendments[edit]

Malformation of a baby born to a mother who had taken thalidomide while pregnant

In the U.S., a push for revisions of the FD&C Act emerged from Congressional hearings led by Senator Estes Kefauver of Tennessee in 1959. The hearings covered a wide range of policy issues, including advertising abuses, questionable efficacy of drugs, and the need for greater regulation of the industry. While momentum for new legislation temporarily flagged under extended debate, a new tragedy emerged that underscored the need for more comprehensive regulation and provided the driving force for the passage of new laws.

On 12 September 1960, an American licensee, the William S. Merrell Company of

Cincinnati, submitted a new drug application for Kevadon (thalidomide), a sedative that had been marketed in Europe since 1956. The FDA medical officer in charge of reviewing the compound, Frances Kelsey, believed that the data supporting the safety of thalidomide was incomplete. The firm continued to pressure Kelsey and the FDA to approve the application until November 1961, when the drug was pulled off the German market because of its association with grave congenital abnormalities. Several thousand newborns in Europe and elsewhere suffered the teratogenic effects of thalidomide. Without approval from the FDA, the firm distributed Kevadon to over 1,000 physicians there under the guise of investigational use. Over 20,000 Americans received thalidomide in this "study," including 624 pregnant patients, and about 17 known newborns suffered the effects of the drug.[citation needed]

The thalidomide tragedy resurrected Kefauver's bill to enhance drug regulation that had stalled in Congress, and the Kefauver-Harris Amendment became law on 10 October 1962. Manufacturers henceforth had to prove to FDA that their drugs were effective as well as safe before they could go on the US market. The FDA received authority to regulate advertising of prescription drugs and to establish good manufacturing practices. The law required that all drugs introduced between 1938 and 1962 had to be effective. An FDA - National Academy of Sciences collaborative study showed that nearly 40 percent of these products were not effective. A similarly comprehensive study of over-the-counter products began ten years later.[71]

1970–1990s[edit]

Statins[edit]

Main article: Discovery and development of statins

In 1971, Akira Endo, a Japanese biochemist working for the pharmaceutical company Sankyo, identified mevastatin (ML-236B), a molecule produced by the fungus Penicillium citrinum, as an inhibitor of HMG-CoA reductase, a critical enzyme used by the body to produce cholesterol. Animal trials showed very good inhibitory effect as in clinical trials, however a long-term study in dogs found toxic effects at higher doses and as a result mevastatin was believed to be too toxic for human use. Mevastatin was never marketed, because of its adverse effects of tumors, muscle deterioration, and sometimes death in laboratory dogs.

P. Roy Vagelos, chief scientist and later CEO of Merck & Co, was interested, and made several trips to Japan starting in 1975. By 1978, Merck had isolated lovastatin (mevinolin, MK803) from the fungus Aspergillus terreus, first marketed in 1987 as Mevacor.[72][73][74]

In April 1994, the results of a Merck-sponsored study, the Scandinavian Simvastatin Survival Study, were announced. Researchers tested simvastatin, later sold by Merck as Zocor, on 4,444 patients with high cholesterol and heart disease. After five years, the study concluded the patients saw a 35% reduction in their cholesterol, and their chances of dying of a heart attack were reduced by 42%.[75] In 1995, Zocor and Mevacor both made Merck over US$1 billion. Endo was awarded the 2006 Japan Prize, and the Lasker-DeBakey Clinical Medical Research Award in 2008. For his "pioneering research into a new class of molecules" for "lowering cholesterol,"[sentence fragment][76][77]

21st Century[edit]

Since several decades, biologics have been rising in importance in comparison with small molecules treatments. The biotech subsector, animal health and the Chinese pharmaceutical sector have also grown substantially. On the organisational side, big international pharma corporations have experienced a substantial decline of their value share. Also, the core generic sector (substitutions for off-patent brands) has been downvalued due to competition.[78]

Torreya estimated the pharmaceutical industry to have a market valuation of US$7.03 trillion by February 2021 from which US$6.1 trillion is the value of the publicly traded companies. Small Molecules modality had 58.2% of the valuation share down from 84.6% in 2003. Biologics was up at 30.5% from 14.5%. The valuation share of Chinese Pharma grew from 2003 to 2021 from 1% to 12% overtaking Switzerland who is now ranked number 3 with 7.7%. The United States had still by far the most valued pharmaceutical industry with 40% of global valuation.[79] 2023 was a year of layoffs for at least 10,000 people across 129 public biotech firms globally, albeit most small firms; this was a significant increase in reductions versus 2022 was in part due to worsening global financial conditions and a reduction in investment by "generalist investors". [80] Private firms also saw a significant reduction in venture capital investment in 2023, continuing a downward trend started in 2021, which also led to a reduction in initial public offerings being floated.[80]

Impact of Mergers and Acquisitions[edit]

A 2022 article articulated this notion succinctly by saying "In the business of drug development, deals can be just as important as scientific breakthroughs", typically referred to as pharmaceutical M&A (for mergers and acquisitions).[81] It highlighted that some of the most impactful of the remedies of the early 21st Century were only made possible through M&A activities, specifically noting Keytruda and Humira.[81]

Research and development[edit]

Main articles: Drug discovery and Drug development

Drug discovery is the process by which potential drugs are discovered or designed. In the past, most drugs have been discovered either by isolating the active ingredient from traditional remedies or by serendipitous discovery. Modern biotechnology often focuses on understanding the metabolic pathways related to a disease state or pathogen, and manipulating these pathways using molecular biology or biochemistry. A great deal of early-stage drug discovery has traditionally been carried out by universities and research institutions.

Drug development refers to activities undertaken after a compound is identified as a potential drug in order to establish its suitability as a medication. Objectives of drug development are to determine appropriate formulation and dosing, as well as to establish safety. Research in these areas generally includes a combination of in vitro studies, in vivo studies, and clinical trials. The cost of late stage development has meant it is usually done by the larger pharmaceutical companies.[82] The pharmaceuticals and biotechnology industry spends more than 15% of its net sales for Research & Development which is in comparison with other industries by far the highest share.[83]

Often, large multinational corporations exhibit vertical integration, participating in a broad range of drug discovery and development, manufacturing and quality control, marketing, sales, and distribution. Smaller organizations, on the other hand, often focus on a specific aspect such as discovering drug candidates or developing formulations. Often, collaborative agreements between research organizations and large pharmaceutical companies are formed to explore the potential of new drug substances. More recently, multi-nationals are increasingly relying on contract research organizations to manage drug development.[84]

The cost of innovation[edit]

Drug discovery and development are very expensive; of all compounds investigated for use in humans only a small fraction are eventually approved in most nations by government-appointed medical institutions or boards, who have to approve new drugs before they can be marketed in those countries. In 2010 18 NMEs (New Molecular Entities) were approved and three biologics by the FDA, or 21 in total, which is down from 26 in 2009 and 24 in 2008. On the other hand, there were only 18 approvals in total in 2007 and 22 back in 2006. Since 2001, the Center for Drug Evaluation and Research has averaged 22.9 approvals a year.[85] This approval comes only after heavy investment in pre-clinical development and clinical trials, as well as a commitment to ongoing safety monitoring. Drugs which fail part-way through this process often incur large costs, while generating no revenue in return. If the cost of these failed drugs is taken into account, the cost of developing a successful new drug (new chemical entity, or NCE), has been estimated at US$1.3 billion[86] (not including marketing expenses). Professors Light and Lexchin reported in 2012, however, that the rate of approval for new drugs has been a relatively stable average rate of 15 to 25 for decades.[87]

Industry-wide research and investment reached a record $65.3 billion in 2009. [88] While the cost of research in the U.S. was about $34.2 billion between 1995 and 2010, revenues rose faster (revenues rose by $200.4 billion in that time).[87]

A study by the consulting firm Bain & Company reported that the cost for discovering, developing and launching (which factored in marketing and other business expenses) a new drug (along with the prospective drugs that fail) rose over a five-year period to nearly $1.7 billion in 2003.[89] According to Forbes, by 2010 development costs were between $4 billion to $11 billion per drug.[90]

Some of these estimates also take into account the opportunity cost of investing capital many years before revenues are realized (see Time-value of money). Because of the very long time needed for discovery, development, and approval of pharmaceuticals, these costs can accumulate to nearly half the total expense. A direct consequence within the pharmaceutical industry value chain is that major pharmaceutical multinationals tend to increasingly outsource risks related to fundamental research, which somewhat reshapes the industry ecosystem with biotechnology companies playing an increasingly important role, and overall strategies being redefined accordingly.[91] Some approved drugs, such as those based on re-formulation of an existing active ingredient (also referred to as Line-extensions) are much less expensive to develop.

Product approval[edit]

In the United States, new pharmaceutical products must be approved by the Food and Drug Administration (FDA) as being both safe and effective. This process generally involves submission of an Investigational New Drug filing with sufficient pre-clinical data to support proceeding with human trials. Following IND approval, three phases of progressively larger human clinical trials may be conducted. Phase I generally studies toxicity using healthy volunteers. Phase II can include pharmacokinetics and dosing in patients, and Phase III is a very large study of efficacy in the intended patient population. Following the successful completion of phase III testing, a New Drug Application is submitted to the FDA. The FDA reviews the data and if the product is seen as having a positive benefit-risk assessment, approval to market the product in the US is granted.[92]

A fourth phase of post-approval surveillance is also often required due to the fact that even the largest clinical trials cannot effectively predict the prevalence of rare side-effects. Postmarketing surveillance ensures that after marketing the safety of a drug is monitored closely. In certain instances, its indication may need to be limited to particular patient groups, and in others the substance is withdrawn from the market completely.

The FDA provides information about approved drugs at the Orange Book site.[93]

In the UK, the Medicines and Healthcare products Regulatory Agency approves and evaluates drugs for use. Normally an approval in the UK and other European countries comes later than one in the USA. Then it is the National Institute for Health and Care Excellence (NICE), for England and Wales, who decides if and how the National Health Service (NHS) will allow (in the sense of paying for) their use. The British National Formulary is the core guide for pharmacists and clinicians.

In many non-US western countries, a 'fourth hurdle' of cost effectiveness analysis has developed before new technologies can be provided. This focuses on the 'efficacy price tag' (in terms of, for example, the cost per QALY) of the technologies in question. In England and Wales NICE decides whether and in what circumstances drugs and technologies will be made available by the NHS, whilst similar arrangements exist with the Scottish Medicines Consortium in Scotland, and the Pharmaceutical Benefits Advisory Committee in Australia. A product must pass the threshold for cost-effectiveness if it is to be approved. Treatments must represent 'value for money' and a net benefit to society.

Orphan drugs[edit]

Main article: Orphan drug

There are special rules for certain rare diseases ("orphan diseases") in several major drug regulatory territories. For example, diseases involving fewer than 200,000 patients in the United States, or larger populations in certain circumstances are subject to the Orphan Drug Act.[94] Because medical research and development of drugs to treat such diseases is financially disadvantageous, companies that do so are rewarded with tax reductions, fee waivers, and market exclusivity on that drug for a limited time (seven years), regardless of whether the drug is protected by patents.

Global sales[edit]

Top 20 drug companies by revenue (2022)[95]

Company	Pharma revenue ($ million)
Pfizer [?]	100,330
Johnson & Johnson [?]	94,940
Roche [?]	66,260
Merck & Co [?]	59,280
Abbvie [?]	58,050
Novartis [?]	50,540
Bristol Myers Squibb [?]	46,160
Sanofi [?]	45,220
AstraZeneca [?]/[?]	44,350

GSK ?	36,150
Takeda ?	30,000
Eli Lilly and Company ?	28,550
Gilead Sciences ?	27,280
Bayer ?	26,640
Amgen ?	26,320
Boehringer Ingelheim ?	25,280
Novo Nordisk ?	25,000
Moderna ?	19,260
Merck KGaA ?	19,160
BioNTech ?	18,200

In 2011, global spending on prescription drugs topped $954 billion, even as growth slowed somewhat in Europe and North America. The United States accounts for more than a third of the global pharmaceutical market, with $340 billion in annual sales followed by the EU and Japan.[96] Emerging markets such as China, Russia, South Korea and Mexico outpaced that market, growing a huge 81 percent.[97][98]

The top ten best-selling drugs of 2013 totaled $75.6 billion in sales, with the anti-inflammatory drug Humira being the best-selling drug worldwide at $10.7 billion in sales. The second and third best selling were Enbrel and Remicade, respectively.[99] The top three best-selling drugs in the United States in 2013 were Abilify ($6.3 billion,) Nexium ($6 billion) and Humira ($5.4 billion).[100] The best-selling drug ever, Lipitor, averaged $13 billion annually and netted $141 billion total over its lifetime before Pfizer's patent expired in November 2011.

IMS Health publishes an analysis of trends expected in the pharmaceutical industry in 2007, including increasing profits in most sectors despite loss of some patents, and new 'blockbuster' drugs on the horizon.[101]

Patents and generics[edit]

Depending on a number of considerations, a company may apply for and be granted a patent for the drug, or the process of producing the drug, granting exclusivity rights typically for about 20 years.[102] However, only after rigorous study and testing, which takes 10 to 15 years on average, will governmental authorities grant permission for the company to market and sell the drug.[103] Patent protection enables the owner of the patent to recover the costs of research and development through high profit margins for the branded drug. When the patent protection for the drug expires, a generic drug is usually developed and sold by a competing company. The development and approval of generics is less expensive, allowing them to be sold at a lower price. Often the owner of the branded drug will introduce a generic version before the patent expires in order to get a head start in the generic market.[104] Restructuring has therefore become routine, driven by the patent expiration of products launched during the industry's "golden era" in the 1990s and companies' failure to develop sufficient new blockbuster products to replace lost revenues.[105]

Prescriptions[edit]

In the U.S., the value of prescriptions increased over the period of 1995 to 2005 by 3.4 billion annually, a 61 percent increase. Retail sales of prescription drugs jumped 250 percent from $72 billion to $250 billion, while the average price of prescriptions more than doubled from $30 to $68.[106]

Marketing[edit]

Main article: Pharmaceutical marketing

Advertising is common in healthcare journals as well as through more mainstream media routes. In some countries, notably the US, they are allowed to advertise directly to the general public. Pharmaceutical companies generally employ salespeople (often called 'drug reps' or, an older term, 'detail men') to market directly and personally to physicians and other healthcare providers. In some countries, notably the US, pharmaceutical companies also employ lobbyists to influence politicians. Marketing of prescription drugs in the US is regulated by the federal Prescription Drug Marketing Act of 1987. The pharmaceutical marketing plan incorporates the spending plans, channels, and thoughts which will take the drug association, and its items and administrations, forward in the current scene.

To healthcare professionals[edit]

The book Bad Pharma also discusses the influence of drug representatives, how ghostwriters are employed by the drug companies to write papers for academics to publish, how independent the academic journals really are, how the drug companies finance doctors' continuing education, and how patients' groups are often funded by industry.[107]

Direct to consumer advertising[edit]

Main article: Direct-to-consumer advertising

Since the 1980s, new methods of marketing for prescription drugs to consumers have become important. Direct-to-consumer media advertising was legalised in the FDA Guidance for Industry on Consumer-Directed Broadcast Advertisements.

Controversies[edit]

Drug marketing and lobbying[edit]

Main articles: Pharmaceutical marketing and Pharmaceutical lobby

There has been increasing controversy surrounding pharmaceutical marketing and influence. There have been accusations and findings of influence on doctors and other health professionals through drug reps including the constant provision of marketing 'gifts' and biased information to health professionals;[108] highly prevalent advertising in journals and conferences; funding independent healthcare organizations and health promotion campaigns; lobbying physicians and politicians (more than any other industry in the US[109]); sponsorship of medical schools or nurse training; sponsorship of continuing educational events, with influence on the curriculum;[110] and hiring physicians as paid consultants on medical advisory boards.

Some advocacy groups, such as No Free Lunch and AllTrials, have criticized the effect of drug marketing to physicians because they say it biases physicians to prescribe the marketed drugs even when others might be cheaper or better for the patient.[111]

There have been related accusations of disease mongering[112] (over-medicalising) to expand the market for medications. An inaugural conference on that subject took place in Australia in 2006.[113] In 2009, the Government-funded National Prescribing Service launched the "Finding Evidence – Recognising Hype" program, aimed at educating GPs on methods for independent drug analysis.[114]

Meta-analyses have shown that psychiatric studies sponsored by pharmaceutical companies are several times more likely to report positive results, and if a drug company employee is involved the effect is even larger.[115][116][117] Influence has also extended to the training of doctors and nurses in medical schools, which is being fought.

It has been argued that the design of the Diagnostic and Statistical Manual of Mental Disorders and the expansion of the criteria represents an increasing medicalization of human nature, or "disease mongering", driven by drug company influence on psychiatry.[118] The potential for direct conflict of interest has been raised, partly because roughly half the authors who selected and defined the DSM-IV psychiatric disorders had or previously had financial relationships with the pharmaceutical industry.[119]

In the US, starting in 2013, under the Physician Financial Transparency Reports (part of the Sunshine Act), the Centers for Medicare & Medicaid Services has to collect information from applicable manufacturers and group purchasing organizations in order to report information about their financial relationships with physicians and hospitals. Data are made public in the Centers for Medicare & Medicaid Services website. The expectation is that relationship between doctors and Pharmaceutical industry will become fully transparent.[120]

In a report conducted by OpenSecrets, there were more than 1,100 lobbyists working in some capacity for the pharmaceutical business in 2017. In the first quarter of 2017, the health products and pharmaceutical industry spent $78 million on lobbying members of the United States Congress.[121]

Medication pricing[edit]

Further information: **Medication costs § Factors**

The pricing of pharmaceuticals is becoming a major challenge for health systems. [122] A November 2020 study by the West Health Policy Center stated that more than 1.1 million senior citizens in the U.S. Medicare program are expected to die prematurely over the next decade because they will be unable to afford their prescription medications, requiring an additional $17.7 billion to be spent annually on avoidable medical costs due to health complications.[123]

Regulatory issues[edit]

Ben Goldacre has argued that regulators – such as the Medicines and Healthcare products Regulatory Agency (MHRA) in the UK, or the Food and Drug Administration (FDA) in the United States – advance the interests of the drug companies rather than the interests of the public due to revolving door exchange of employees between the regulator and the companies and friendships develop between regulator and company employees. [124] He argues that regulators do not require that new drugs offer an improvement over what is already available, or even that they be particularly effective.[124]

Others have argued that excessive regulation suppresses therapeutic innovation and that the current cost of regulator-required clinical trials prevents the full exploitation of new genetic and biological knowledge for the treatment of human disease. A 2012 report by the President's Council of Advisors on Science and Technology made several key recommendations to reduce regulatory burdens to new drug development, including 1) expanding the FDA's use of accelerated approval processes, 2) creating an expedited approval pathway for drugs intended for use in narrowly defined populations, and 3) undertaking pilot projects designed to evaluate the feasibility of a new, adaptive drug approval process.[125]

Pharmaceutical fraud[edit]

See also: List of largest pharmaceutical settlements in the United States

	The examples and perspective in this section **deal primarily with the United States and do not represent a worldwide view of the subject**. You may improve this section, discuss the issue on the talk page, or create a new section, as appropriate. *(August 2015)* *(Learn how and when to remove this template message)*

Pharmaceutical fraud involves deceptions which bring financial gain to a pharmaceutical company. It affects individuals and public and private insurers. There are several different schemes[126] used to defraud the health care system which are particular to the pharmaceutical industry. These include: Good Manufacturing Practice (GMP) Violations, Off Label Marketing, Best Price Fraud, CME Fraud, Medicaid Price Reporting, and Manufactured Compound Drugs.[127] Of this amount $2.5 billion was recovered through False Claims Act cases in FY 2010. Examples of fraud cases include the GlaxoSmithKline $3 billion settlement, Pfizer $2.3 billion settlement and Merck & Co. $650 million settlement. Damages from fraud can be recovered by use of the False Claims Act, most commonly under the qui tam provisions which rewards an individual for being a "whistleblower", or relator (law).[128]

Every major company selling atypical antipsychotics—Bristol-Myers Squibb, Eli Lilly and Company, Pfizer, AstraZeneca and Johnson & Johnson—has either settled recent government cases, under the False Claims Act, for hundreds of millions of dollars or is currently under investigation for possible health care fraud. Following charges of illegal marketing, two of the settlements set records in 2009 for the largest criminal fines ever imposed on corporations. One involved Eli Lilly's antipsychotic Zyprexa, and the other involved Bextra, an anti-inflammatory medication used for arthritis. In the Bextra case, the government also charged Pfizer with illegally marketing another antipsychotic, Geodon; Pfizer settled that part of the claim for $301 million, without admitting any wrongdoing.[129]

On 2 July 2012, GlaxoSmithKline pleaded guilty to criminal charges and agreed to a $3 billion settlement of the largest health-care fraud case in the U.S. and the largest payment by a drug company.[130] The settlement is related to the company's illegal promotion of prescription drugs, its failure to report safety data,[131] bribing doctors, and promoting medicines for uses for which they were not licensed. The drugs involved were Paxil, Wellbutrin, Advair, Lamictal, and Zofran for off-label, non-covered uses. Those and the drugs Imitrex, Lotronex, Flovent, and Valtrex were involved in the kickback scheme.[132][133][134]

The following is a list of the four largest settlements reached with pharmaceutical companies from 1991 to 2012, rank ordered by the size of the total settlement. Legal claims against the pharmaceutical industry have varied widely over the past two decades, including Medicare and Medicaid fraud, off-label promotion, and inadequate manufacturing practices.[135][136]

Company	Settlement	Violation(s)	Year	Product(s)	Laws allegedly violated (if applicable)

GlaxoSmit hKline[137]	$3 billion	Off-label promotion / failure to disclose safety data	2012	Avandia/ Wellbutrin/ Paxil	False Claims Act/FDCA
Pfizer[138]	$2.3 billion	Off-label promotion /kickbacks	2009	Bextra/ Geodon/ Zyvox/ Lyrica	False Claims Act/FDCA
Abbott Laboratori es[139]	$1.5 billion	Off-label promotion	2012	Depakote	False Claims Act/FDCA
Eli Lilly[140]	$1.4 billion	Off-label promotion	2009	Zyprexa	False Claims Act/FDCA

Physician roles[edit]

In May 2015, the New England Journal of Medicine emphasized the importance of pharmaceutical industry-physician interactions for the development of novel treatments, and argued that moral outrage over industry malfeasance had unjustifiably led many to overemphasize the problems created by financial conflicts of interest. The article noted that major healthcare organizations, such as National Center for Advancing Translational Sciences of the National Institutes of Health, the President's Council of Advisors on Science and Technology, the World Economic Forum, the Gates Foundation, the Wellcome Trust, and the Food and Drug Administration had encouraged greater interactions between physicians and industry in order to improve benefits to patients.[141][142]

Response to COVID-19[edit]

In November 2020 several pharmaceutical companies announced successful trials of COVID-19 vaccines, with efficacy of 90 to 95% in preventing infection. Per company announcements and data reviewed by external analysts, these vaccines are priced at $3 to $37 per dose.[143] The Wall Street Journal ran an editorial calling for this achievement to be recognized with a Nobel Peace Prize.[144]

Doctors Without Borders warned that high prices and monopolies on medicines, tests, and vaccines would prolong the pandemic and cost lives. They urged governments to prevent profiteering, using compulsory licenses as needed, as had already been done by Canada, Chile, Ecuador, Germany, and Israel.[145]

On 20 February, 46 US lawmakers called for the US government not to grant monopoly rights when giving out taxpayer development money for any coronavirus vaccines and treatments, to avoid giving exclusive control of prices and availability to private manufacturers.[146]

In the United States the government signed agreements in which research and development and/or the building of manufacturing plants for potential COVID-19 therapeutics was subsidized. Typically, the agreement involved the government taking ownership of a certain number of doses of the product without further payment. For example, under the auspices of Operation Warp Speed in the United States, the government subsidized research related to COVID-19 vaccines and therapeutics at Regeneron,[147] Johnson and Johnson, Moderna, AstraZeneca, Novavax, Pfizer, and GSK. Typical terms involved research subsidies of $400 million to $2 billion, and included government ownership of the first 100 million doses of any COVID-19 vaccine successfully developed.[148]

American pharmaceutical company Gilead sought and obtained orphan drug status for remdesivir from the US Food and Drug Administration (FDA) on 23 March 2020. This provision is intended to encourage the development of drugs affecting fewer than 200,000 Americans by granting strengthened and extended legal monopoly rights to the manufacturer, along with waivers on taxes and government fees.[149] [150] Remdesivir is a candidate for treating COVID-19; at the time the status was granted, fewer than 200,000 Americans had COVID-19, but numbers were climbing rapidly as the COVID-19 pandemic reached the US, and crossing the threshold soon was considered inevitable.[149][150] Remdesivir was developed by Gilead with over $79 million in U.S. government funding.[150] In May 2020, Gilead announced that it would provide the first 940,000 doses of remdesivir to the federal government free of charge. [151] After facing strong public reactions, Gilead gave up the "orphan drug" status for remdesivir on 25 March.[152] Gilead retains 20-year remdesivir patents in more than 70 countries.[145] In May 2020, the company further announced that it was in discussions with several generics companies to provide rights to produce remdesivir for developing countries, and with the Medicines Patent Pool to provide broader generic access.[153] Developing world[edit]

Patents[edit]

Patents have been criticized in the developing world, as they are thought[who?] to reduce access to existing medicines.[154] Reconciling patents and universal access to medicine would require an efficient international policy of price discrimination. Moreover, under the TRIPS agreement of the World Trade Organization, countries must allow pharmaceutical products to be patented. In 2001, the WTO adopted the Doha Declaration, which indicates that the TRIPS agreement should be read with the goals of public health in mind, and allows some methods for circumventing pharmaceutical monopolies: via compulsory licensing or parallel imports, even before patent expiration. [155]

In March 2001, 40 multi-national pharmaceutical companies brought litigation against South Africa for its Medicines Act, which allowed the generic production of antiretroviral drugs (ARVs) for treating HIV, despite the fact that these drugs were on-patent.[156] HIV was and is an epidemic in South Africa, and ARVs at the time cost between US$10,000 and US$15,000 per patient per year. This was unaffordable for most South African citizens, and so the South African government committed to providing ARVs at prices closer to what people could afford. To do so, they would need to ignore the patents on drugs and produce generics within the country (using a compulsory license), or import them from abroad. After international protest in favour of public health rights (including the collection of 250,000 signatures by Médecins Sans Frontières), the governments of several developed countries (including The Netherlands, Germany, France, and later the US) backed the South African government, and the case was dropped in April of that year.[157]

In 2016, GlaxoSmithKline (the world's sixth largest pharmaceutical company) announced that it would be dropping its patents in poor countries so as to allow independent companies to make and sell versions of its drugs in those areas, thereby widening the public access to them.[158] GlaxoSmithKline published a list of 50 countries they would no longer hold patents in, affecting one billion people worldwide. - wiki

Stress and Allergic Diseases

Ninabahen D. Dave, MBBS, Clinical fellow, Lianbin Xiang, MD, Assistant Professor of Medicine, Kristina E. Rehm, PhD, Postdoctoral Research Fellow, and Gailen D. Marshall, Jr., MD, PhD, Professor of Medicine and Pediatrics
Author information Copyright and License information PMC Disclaimer

The publisher's final edited version of this article is available at Immunol Allergy Clin North Am

Go to:

Summary

Allergy describes a constellation of clinical diseases that affect up to 30% of the world's population. It is characterized by production of allergen specific IgE which bind to mast cells and initiate a cascade of molecular and cellular events that affect the respiratory tract (rhinitis and asthma) skin (dermatitis, urticaria) and multi systems (anaphylaxis) to a variety of allergens including pollens, mold spores, animal danders, insect stings, foods and drugs. The underlying pathophysiology involves immunoregulatory dysfunctions similar to those noted in highly stressed populations. The relationships in terms of potentials for intervention are discussed.

Keywords: allergy, asthma, stress, immunoregulation

Go to:

Introduction

Allergic diseases such as asthma, allergic rhinitis, food allergies, and insect sting allergies have been described since early in recorded history. A clinical condition with asthma-like symptoms was described 3500 years ago in an Egyptian manuscript dubbed the Ebers Papyrus1. In 1906, Austrian pediatrician Clemens Von Pirquet first used the word *allergy* to describe the strange, non-disease-related symptoms that some diphtheria patients developed when treated with a horse serum antitoxins[2]. Subsequently the field of clinical allergy developed, based upon multiple discoveries: the clinical effectiveness of allergen immunotherapy[3], mast cell granules as the major source of histamine in humans [4], identification of IgE as the allergen-specific initiator of allergic reactions[5] and the lipoxygenase-based leukotriene cascade as the clinically described slow reacting substance of anaphylaxis[6] . These and other discoveries have ushered in the modern day practice of allergy and clinical immunology that cares for up to 30% of people in western societies who suffer with various allergic diseases including hay fever (allergic rhinitis), asthma , atopic dermatitis, food allergy, drug allergy and the life threatening systemic mast cell-mediated reaction known as anaphylaxis.

Allergy has been defined as the result of immune reaction to specific types of mostly protein antigens known as allergens. Atopy, genetically mediated predisposition to produce specific IgE following exposure to allergens, is clinically defined as having evidence of allergic sensitization to at least one environmental allergen. Atopy is a fundamental component of the pathogenesis of allergic disorders. Although the clinical manifestations can be distinct between affected organs in a patient and even the same organ among different patients, allergic diseases share a common pathophysiology resulting from immune dysregulation and subsequent potentially harmful inflammation (so called hypersensitivity disease).

In recent decades, many studies have shown multiple links between nervous, endocrine and immune systems. The field of psychoneuroimmunology (PNI) has and continues to describe various links between behavior, neuroendocrine functions, immune responses and health. Excessive psychological stress and allergic disorder have been linked together in clinical practice for centuries. Many allergic conditions have long been considered psychosomatic disorders which had worsened outcomes in patienst with high levels of psychosocial stress. For example, asthma was commonly referred to in most early medical texts as "asthma nervosa" based upon the belief that , in many children, it was the result of a conversion reaction from living with a histrionic mothers. Early descriptions of atopic dermatitis used the term "neurodermatitis" due to belief that the itch and scratch cycle which results in a rash, was related primarily to "nerves" and emotion.

Thus it is not surprising that allergy, one of the most prevalent of all human disease categories and psychological stress are related. This chapter will explore the relationships between allergic diseases and stress and suggest future mechanism-based research directions to develop therapeutic and even prophylactic approaches to disease management with stress-based interventions.

Go to:

Stress

Stress can be thought of as a psychophysiological process that is a product of both the appraisal of a given situation to assess potential adversity and the ability (either perceived or actual) to cope with that potentially adverse situations. The events/situations posing the potential threat are called stressors. Situations can be experiences in daily life, including daily hassles (ordinary stressors from interactions with family, neighborhood and/or school/ in the work place) as well as major life events, which may be either positive or negative such as a large promotion that requires significantly increased physical and mental effort or losing one's job resulting in financial crisis. Based on their duration, stressors are often considered acute (minutes to hours), subacute (less than one month duration) or chronic (months to years). Intensity of the stress, even when acute, may have longer lasting effects that can ovelap with a less intense stressor lasting for a longer period of time. Further, repetitive acute stressors (the same ones or even different ones) may, with time and intensity, have similar effects to that of a single long term stressor.

PNI research focuses primarily on the understanding of the relationships between psychological stress perception (both conscious and subconscious) and downstream behavior, endocrine and immune changes occurring in response to that stress perception. The brain perceives and responds to stressors and determines both the behavioral and physiological responses. The typical host response to isolated episodes of acute stress is adaptive for the protection of the host whereas chronic stress can lead to dysregulation of the mediators and exacerbate underlying inflammatory disease pathophysiology. There are multiple reported factors that can impact this cause-and-effect relationship including genetic background (which may include gender and racial differences), previous life experiences and past/present environmental exposures. Of note, the same factors have been reported to impact the incidence and severity of allergic diseases as well.

Go to:

Adverse Impact of Stress on Health

A common clinical observation is the often adverse relationship between stress and human diseases10. Various sources have estimated that up to 75% of all visits to physician's offices are stress-related. This appears to be particularly true in relationship to other immune-based dysfunction such as increased susceptibility to infections and various autoimmune diseases. Stress is also implicated in morbidity and mortality of other inflammatory based diseases such as cancer, HIV/AIDS, inflammatory bowel disease and even immune senescence associated with aging. Stress may also cause persistent increases in sympathetic nervous system activity, including increase blood pressure, heart rate and catecholamine secretion as well as platelet aggregation which may explain, at least in part, the known association between stress, immune alteration and cardiovascular disease. In addition, altered sleep can modulate stress-health relationship. Sleep disturbance have been associated with adverse physical health outcomes including increase morbidity and mortality compared to population with adequate pattern and duration of sleep. Other pathologies associated with allostatic overload from chronic stress include depression[11], tendencies towards unhealthy behavior[12], diabetes[13], dyslipidemia[13]; irritable bowel syndrome[14] and cerebrovascular accidents[15].

Go to:

Stress and Allergic Disease

Stress-induced exacerbation of existing allergic disease

Clinical observations implicating the adverse effects of psychological stress on disease activity in allergic patients is supported by studies that have demonstrated that allergic responses can be modulated by mood and psychological stressors. Gauci et al found a correlation between the Minnesota Multiphasic Personality Inventory distress related scales and skin reactivity in response to allergen challenge [16]. In addition, different studies have shown that the impact of life event, negative support and current mood disorder were associated with increased rate of asthma hospital admission[17] and negative life event and negative rumination were associated with asthma morbidity[18]. Further, behavior problems and family conflicts preceded the development of asthma in multiple pediatric populations[19, 20].

Another study showed enhancement of allergic inflammatory responses with natural stress exposure[21]. Sputum eosinophils levels in 20 otherwise healthy college students with asthma were evaluated before and after an allergen challenge. Although there were no baseline differences before antigen challenge at low (mid semester) and high (during final examinations) stress exposures, sputum eosinophils counts rose higher and persisted longer in response to allergen challenge during final examinations. Additionally blood eosinophils levels were significantly higher both before and after challenge during final examinations compared to mid semester samples.

Stress and incidence of allergic disease

The potential for adverse impact of maternal stress on immunity in a developing fetus and possible postnatal disease occurrence is concerning. Psychological maternal stress is increasingly considered a possible perinatal programming agent. Perinatal programming occurs when characteristics of the *in utero* environment, independent of genetic susceptibility, influence fetal development to permanently organize or imprint physiological systems. Intrauterine stress hormone levels (both maternal and fetal) are thought to rise with prenatal maternal stress. Since fetal immunity initially is involved primarily in self-nonself programming to prevent future autoimmunity, such prenatal stress hormone exposure may alter natural immunoregulatory mechanisms such that the child has increased risk for developing various inflammatory diseases including allergy and asthma. Various animal and human studies have shown linkage between maternal stress and immune dysregulation in children. Wright *et al* reported that increased stress in early childhood was associated with an atopic immune profile in children predisposed to atopy-asthma (i.e. positive family history for atopy) [22]. They have also shown that caregiver stress can increase the incidence of early childhood wheeze independent of caregiver smoking, breast-feeding behaviors, allergen exposure, birth weight or lower respiratory tract infections[22, 23]. These findings indicate a significant potential impact of psychological stress on childhood wheeze and subsequent development of clinical allergy and asthma. These studies and others support a strong role for stress in exacerbation and possible etiology of allergic diseases.

Go to:

Immunopathophysiology of allergic disease

IgE-mediated allergic disorders may manifest clinically as any combination of conjunctivitis, rhinitis, asthma, atopic dermatitis, food and/or drug intolerance and/or anaphylaxis. It has been well recognized that atopic dermatitis and food allergies are often the earliest manifestation of atopic predisposition in a young child. Nearly 50% of children with atopic dermatitis develop asthma and 75% develop allergic rhinitis. The *allergic march* is a sequential or sometimes simultaneous expression of two or three of the above mentioned allergic disorders in an individual progresses from infancy to adolescence and adulthood[24].

The prevalence of allergy and asthma has increased in nearly all countries worldwide and is more common in Westernized and economically developed countries. As many as 1 in 3 individual suffer from some form of allergic disorder[25]. Development of allergic disorders involves multiple factors including genetic components (family history) , both indoor (dust mite, molds, animal danders) and outdoor (pollens, ozone and diesel exhaust) environmental exposure – as well as other life style factors including maternal diet, reproductive physiology and birth outcomes, breast feeding, child nutrition and vitamin D level, obesity, physical activity and psychological stress.

Atopic Dermatitis (AD)

AD is a chronic relapsing inflammatory skin disease commonly associated with respiratory allergy[26]. It is the most common chronic skin disease of young children, with lifetime prevalence in US schoolchildren up to 17%. Itching and scratching are the hallmark of this disease. Itching is often worse at night leading to chronic sleep disturbance in patient and immediate family members and is a source of significant psychological and physiological stress. When patients with AD become upset, they tend to itch even more, probably secondary to flushing of the skin due to vasodilatation induced by neurogenic peptides, followed by increased histamine and prostaglandin E2 release [27]. Distribution of the rash on the face and extensor aspects in infant and young children, changing to more flexural surface involvement in older agesis a classical finding of AD. . About ninety-five percent of patients with AD become colonized by a ubiquitous pathogen, *Staphylococcus aureus* which releases toxins that can act as superantigens and stimulate marked inflammatory responses as well as specific IgE production. Patients with AD are prone to recurrent bacterial (impetigo), fungal (tinea) and viral (Herpes Simplex molluscum contagiosum) skin infections. Allergens, irritants (wool, soap, detergents, heat and humidity with sweating), infections and certain foods can worsen eczema[28, 29]. The impact on self esteem and social interactions of both children and adults with this condition cannot be underestimated and may account for some of the chronicity commonly seen in these patients[30].

Allergic Rhinitis Allergic rhinitis (AR) is a debilitating disease that currently affects up to 30% of the world population . Classical symptoms of AR include profuse watery rhinorrhea, sneezing, itchy nose, and congestion. Post nasal drip might be present and cause cough or persistent throat clearing. Sometimes AR patients can also experience itchy conjunctiva, ears and throat. . AR is generally classified as seasonal (SAR) and perennial (PAR), based on presence or absence of seasonality and the source of allergens triggering the symptoms.but more recently has been classified based on duration and severity of symptoms as mild intermittent, mild persistent, moderate or severe intermittent, and moderate or severe persistent to aid with choice of therapy.

Non-allergic triggers like strong odors, tobacco smoke, and temperature changes can stimulate symptoms in AR patients similar to those induced by allergens., suggesting hyper responsiveness which is more commonly reported in lower airways. Neural reflex arcs in the upper airways, when challenged with allergens, can incite lower airway bronchospasm. These observations gave rise to the concept of "one linked airway" which addresses the observed connection between nasal and pulmonary symptoms in allergic individuals."[31]. Patient with allergic rhinitis can often have sleep impairment due to nasal obstruction which typically worsens at night. Fatigue, malaise, and impairment of work and school performance are common when AR symptoms are severe[32]. Patients with AR are more prone to upper respiratory infections during periods of high psychological stress[33].

Asthma Asthma is defined as a chronic inflammatory disorder of the airways in which many cells and cellular elements play a role. The chronic inflammation causes an associated increase in airway hyper responsiveness that leads to recurrent episodes of wheezing, breathlessness, chest tightness, and coughing, particularly at night or in the early morning. These episodes are usually associated with widespread but variable airflow obstruction that is often reversible either spontaneously or with treatment[34]. Based on 2005 NHIS results, an estimated 32.6 million Americans have received an asthma diagnosis during their lifetimes, an increase in prevalence by 16% from 1997[35]. Atopy, particularly to house dust mites and cockroaches and family history of allergy or asthma are known risk factors for asthma. Common symptoms described by patients include cough, wheezing, chest tightness, dyspnea and occasionally chest pain. In up to 15% of asthma patients, dry cough may be the only presenting respiratory symptom.. Exercise induced bronchospasm is present in almost 90% of all asthmatics which results from rapid change of airway temperatures with increased tidal volumes and mouth breathing. Any and all of these symptoms have been reported to be worsened in asthma patients experiencing high stress levels.

Acute exacerbation of asthma can be triggered by upper and lower respiratory tract infections (specially viruses such as rhinovirus, influenza, parainfluenza, respiratory syncital viruses), changes in weather, significant allergen exposure in sensitized individuals, cold air, exercise, various stressful situations and hormonal changes related to menses in some women. Approximately five thousands deaths occur in the United States from asthma annually.

Go to:

B. Altered Immunity in Allergic Diseases

For purposes of this discussion, allergy or immediate hypersensitivity describes a series of immune based reactions occurring as a result of the induction of allergen specific IgE that binds to mast cells via high affinity FcεR1 receptors. Subsequent re-exposure to the inciting allergen causes a cross-linking of the mast cells-bound IgE with activation and release of the mast cell contents such as histamine, leukotrines, tryptase, chymase, kininogenase, and heparin within 5–60 minutes of exposure. These mediators can induce vasodilatation and vascular leaks, causing mucosal edema, increased mucus gland secretions, nasal and/or bronchial congestion and occlusion resulting in various clinical signs and symptoms. . Late phase allergic reactions can occur six to twenty-four hours after initial exposure following the recruitment and migration of inflammatory cells like eosinophils, basophils, neutrophils, T lymphocytes, and macrophages to the target tissues (skin, nose, lung, gastrointestinal tract, and/ or blood vessels). These result in more persistent symptoms. TH2 cytokines play a critical role in orchestrating ongoing inflammation.

Chronic changes seen in airways of asthmatics include smooth muscle hypertrophy and hyperplasia, goblet cell hyperplasia, submucosal gland hypertrophy, neovascularization, thickening of reticular basement membrane, and fibrotic changes with collagen deposition[49]. Airway smooth muscle hyper responsiveness is another hallmark of asthma which might precede, accompany and sometimes be independent of airway inflammation, suggesting heterogeneity of asthma phenotypes. While, increase transepithelial water losses, defective skin barrier function, allergen-and-infection-induced inflammation, and abnormal regeneration of damaged skin are the characteristics of atopic dermatitis[29].

As already discussed, the production of the IgE is under the direct control of type 2 cytokine production with IL-4 and IL-13 being responsible for isotype switch from IgM to IgE. IL-4 is also a mast cell growth factor and IL-5 is a major chemotactic, growth and activation factor for eosinophils, which are a central component of allergic inflammation[50]. Thus, clinical allergic diseases can be viewed as immunoregulatory imbalances where Th2 cytokines predominates[51].

Dysregulation of Th1 and Th2 cytokine balance play a central role in the immunopathology of allergic diseases. . Allergen-specific T-cell clones from atopic patients have a much higher percentage of TH2 or TH0 type compared with healthy individuals, which tend to have more TH1[40, 52]. Finally, treatment of allergic rhinitis with allergen immunotherapy has been demonstrated to result in a shifting of overall Th1 and Th2 cytokine levels toward a more balanced Th1/Th2 response, which correlates with decreases in clinical disease activity [53]. These mechanism studies would support the theory that physiological states associated with type II cytokine environment could exacerbates asthmatic and allergic diseases.

Since we and others have shown that chronic psychosocial stress is associated with an altered Th1/Th2 balance toward a Th2 predominance, it is not surprising from an immune standpoint that stress can exacerbate allergic diseases such as AR, AD and asthma. Such observations lead to interventions for these diseases that are based upon the notion of managing (if not reducing) stress as a means to control symptoms and, perhaps in the future, prevent the appearance of allergic diseases in the most susceptible individuals. (Fig 1)

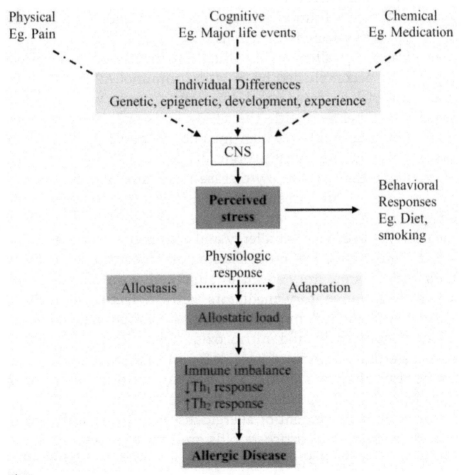

Fig 1
Stress-Allergic Disease Paradigm

Go to:

Management of Allergic Disease

Clinical principles for managing allergic diseases include of

1. Avoidance of exposure to known allergic and non-allergic triggers
2. Controlled exposure to allergens that cannot be totally avoided (i.e. airborn pollens, mold spores, dust mite proteins)
3. Pharmacotherapy to treat mast cell mediated symptoms and reduce allergic inflammation
4. Allergen Immunotherapy for upper and lower airway disease in selected individuals

Identification of allergens to which an individual is sensitive is typically accomplished by *in vitro* (ImmunoCAP-RAST) or *in vivo* (skin prick or intradermal skin testing) assays when feasible, which is correlated with the clinical history of symptoms. Environmental control, which includes improve symptoms of susceptible patients with allergic diseases54. The general goal of pharmacotherapy for any disease is to minimize the impact of the disease on patient's life with minimal adverse side effects of the medications. There are many different types of medications used to treat allergy and asthmabut corticosteroids are the most effective anti-inflammatory medications. C exert their anti-inflammatory effects by suppressing the expression of a host of inflammatory mediators (growth factors, cytokines, chemokines) and inflammatory enzymes involved in metabolism of arachidonic acid and nitric oxide (NO). Topical forms of corticosteroids (i.e. inhaled steroids for asthma, intranasal steroid sprays for allergic rhinitis and topical steroid crèmes and ointments for allergic dermatitis) represent first line therapy in everyday management of allergic diseases. In addition, short courses of systemic corticosteroids are typically used for acute exacerbations of allergic diseases . Inhaled bronchodilators (β2-agonist) and anticholinergic are also used in management of acute asthma exacerbations . Antihistamines in oral, intranasal and ocular forms as well as leukotriene receptor antagonists are also used in management of various allergic diseases.

Immunotherapy for inhaled allergens induces regulatory T cells that dampen the allergic responses to allergens. Two forms of immunotherapy, Subcutaneous Immunotherapy (SCIT) and Sublingual Immunotherapy (SCIT) are in use currently. SCIT is the conventional immunotherapy which involves injecting gradually increasing doses of an allergen that a given patient is sensitized to and has history of problems on exposure followed by a maintenance therapy with the same. Studies showed that the global assessment of improvement with SLIT was significantly better than placebo although only half the difference recorded in the SCIT study[55, 56]. Use of recombinant technology in immunotherapy is under development and in experimental phase.

Immunomodulatory therapy with anti-IgE is a major advancement in the field of allergy and immunology. It reduces the rate of clinically significant asthma exacerbations irrespective of baseline oral corticosteroid use, concomitant treatment with other controller medications and patient characteristics.

Go to:

Impact of Stress on Immune system

The link between the brain and immune system involves two main pathways: the autonomic nervous system (ANS) and the-hyphophyseal-pituitary - adrenal (HPA) axis. Perception of stress leads to activation of HPA system which begins with the secretion of corticotrophin releasing hormone (CRH) which in turn induces the secretion of adrenocortictrophic hormone (ACTH) by the anterior lobe of the pituitary lobe. ACTH activates the secretion of corticoids by the adrenal cortex and catecholamines (adrenalin and noradrenalin) by the adrenal medulla. The catecholamines and corticoids suppress the production of IL-12 by the antigen-presenting cells which is a primary TH1 cytokine-inducing inducing stimulus[57]. Corticoids can also exert a direct effect upon TH2 cells thus increasing the production of IL-4, IL-10 and IL-13[58]. The end result is the predominance of a TH2 cell mediated response which would favor an "allergic" inflammatory response in a susceptible individual.

The ANS is composed of sympathetic (adrenergic, noradrenergic) and the parasympathetic (cholinergic) systems in the CNS with noradrenalin and acetyl choline as neurotransmitters, respectively and the non-adrenergic, non-cholinergic (peptidergic) system primarily located in the gastrointestinal tract. The main peptides of this system are vasoactive intestinal peptides (VIP), substance P (SP) and calcitonin gene-related peptide (CGRP). The innervation of important organs and systems related to the immune system such as the liver, spleen, thymus gland, bone marrow, lymph nodes, skin, digestive tract, and respiratory apparatus is by postsynaptic ANS[59]. Most immune system cells have surface membrane receptors for varying combinations of neurotransmitters, neuropeptides and hormones[60].

The CNS modulates immune system through neurotransmitters (acetyle choline, noradrenalin, serotonin, histamine, γ-aminobutyric acid (GABA), glutamic acid), neuropeptides (ACTH, prolactin, vasopressin, bradykinin, somatostatin, VIP, SP, neuropeptide Y, encephalin, endorphin), neurological growth factors (neuron growth factor (NGF)), and hormones (adrenalin and corticoids) whereas the immune system can also modulate CNS function via various molecules including cytokines (tumor necrosis factor alpha – TNFα and TGFβ), chemokines (interferons) and nitric oxide (NO)[61]. Perception of acute stress stimulates the locus ceruleus which secretes noradrenalin. Noradrenalin activates the sympathetic nervous system leading to decrease production of IL-12 as described earlier.

Neuropeptides including SP, CGRP and VIP are potent vasodilators and also increases vascular permeability. SP increases the production of TNFα and IL-12 by monocytes and macrophages. SP and CRH can degranulate mast cells within inflammatory foci. All of the above processes lead to inflammatory changes[62].

SP and CGRP have been identified in bronchial mucosa as neurogenic inflammatory agents[63]. In addition, Neurokinin-1, receptor for SP, is located on bronchial vessels, bronchial smooth muscle, epithelial cells, submucosal glands and immune cells. Stress likely exerts its effect on bronchial mucosa of asthmatics by varying combinations of impacting number and function of various immune/inflammatory cells as well as direct action on bronchial mucosa[64].

Increased tissue levels of neurotrophins, acting as nerve growth factors, have been described in different respiratory and dermatologic allergic disorders. They act on immune cells, structural cells (keratinocytes, epithelial cells) and can increase angiogenesis[65]. Eosinophils and submucosal glands of the nasal mucosa are a major source of neurotrophins[66] which have been shown to regulate eosinophil survival in the lungs, increase production of specific IgE and change the cytokines profile towards TH2 predominance.

These findings and others demonstrate that interactions between the CNS and immune systems are complex and bidirectional.

Go to:
Addressing stress in comprehensive allergic disease management

Similar to allergic diseases, progression of the other immune-based diseases such as cardiovascular disease, diabetes mellitus, development of AIDS in HIV+ patients and certain malignancies has been suggested for high-stress population. Thus it follows that managing stress in these patients could be expected to have salutatory effects on their underlying disease course.

Strategies for stress management as part of a comprehensive treatment plan should involve identification of high-risk population or , ideally, individuals. Current efforts are underway in our group and others to identify biomarkers that would categorize individuals into risk categories for adverse effects of psychological stress on their immune system which, in turn, would effect risk for or activity of underlying immune-based diseases. The categorization would be followed by (ideally) individualized prophylactic interventions in the highest at-risk individuals to prevent immune based diseases or therapeutic intervention in the diseased individuals with the intent to minimize the immunoregulatory imbalance that characterizes chronic stress –induced immune changes.

Stress reduction/elimination would be the most desirable intervention but is often difficult to achieve in our fast paced, high pressure societies. Accordingly, , methods (psychological, physiological, pharmacological or some combination) to improve individual coping abilities to stressful situations are more likely to be clinically valuable as a core of the interventional strategies for stress management[67].

Many studies have shown the encouraging effects of psychological interventions on clinical outcome in allergic diseases. Smyth et al showed that expressive writing about stressful events was associated with symptom reduction in asthma patients. Biofeedback as well as mental imagery has a positive role in asthma management[68-70]. In a systematic review, Huntley et al. described that relaxation therapy had a positive effect on asthma outcomes[71]. While Psychotherapy can reduce the number of asthma exacerbations and ER visits in depressed asthma patients[72]. Although evidence suggests that these interventions result in restoring a more normal Th1/Th2 balance , further research is warranted to prove a direct link between clinical improvement and immune changes following psychological interventions in allergic diseases.

Physiological interventions for allergic diseases include various forms of exercise programs as well as complementary and alternative medicine techniques such as acupuncture, chiropractic and applied kinesiology all of which may work, at least in part, by their impact on the underlying stress of the individual.. So far, well designed studies have not shown a clear benefit of complementary and alternative medicine interventions, perhaps secondary to the robust placebo effect with subsequent psychophysiological impact on immunity[73, 74] and thus likely on allergic diseases[75]. Based upon the severity of the underlying dysfunction, exercise had varied effects on immune function. Exercise training program are well tolerated in children with mild-to-moderate asthma and improves both aerobic and anaerobic fitness[76]. Exercise rehabilitation programs improve aerobic conditioning, ventilatory capacity as well as decrease hyperpnea of exercise occurred in patients with mild asthma[77]. But, as a caution, excessive exercise can lead to an exacerbation of disease in poorly controlled asthmatic patients.

Reported pharmacological interventions for stress have mainly included psychoactive agents . Both tricyclic and SSRI antidepressants may have a therapeutic role in asthma by suppressing production of proinflammatory cytokines, inducing production of anti-inflammatory molecules and/or preventing the effects of these inflammatory molecules on the brain[78]. Both adult and child/adolescent populations with asthma appear to have a high prevalence of anxiety disorders[79]. In addition, anxiolytic drugs may have beneficial in increasing the quality of asthma therapy in asthmatics with anxiety disorder[80].

Psychological stress increases superoxide release[81]. This finding suggests a potential prophylactic role of anti-oxidant agents like Vitamin C and E against stress-induced immune changes. Studies have shown vitamin C and vitamin E can reduce immunoregulatory imbalances noted in stressed individuals[82].

Thus, many different approaches with proven or likely beneficial effects are available to modulate stress and thus immune function to have positive effects in allergic patients.

CLEANLINESS VS GODLINESS

Kingdom of god is within you, the Kemetic mysteries are the mystery school science, and todays chemistry. God is and acts through the periodic table. The importance of Light can't be overstated here, 137 or 1/137 being the number that not only describes the interaction of Light and Matter but also how light holds atoms together to form Matter.

I think we forget about the second feature. Thomas of Aquinas is known to have coined the term "Cleanliness is close to goodliness" and we may have to debunk him! Light is pure. Sure. The thing is living creatures are made out of dirt, bacteria and virus.

Any substance that is anti dirt is toxic, any substance that kills bacteria can be harmful and any substance (save iodine) that denatures a virus can be dangerous. Can be and are, are two different things before I am misquoted.

We discuss in quite a few books the relationship of the environment on the process of Cellular development. This conversation maybe the first we have on this aspect of King's Disease.

The elements of God, the dirt, are being excluded from peoples lives because they conflict with Technology! You heard me, the environment is becoming overly sanitized because of technology which has started a amazing trend in profit for the Pharmaceutical Industry, at the cost of the health of the people. Children are mostly feeling the blow!

Imagine not being able to play outside or in school, not being able to have a PBJ on fear of death, not being able to come in contact with other kids.... Welcome to the world of Allergies, and if god made man out of dirt, then this is the birth of the Ungodly!

The Bible constantly speaks of Horizontal Gene Transfer, the dead shall rise and their memories. This is important to understand, HGT is a active component of life. Disease and immunity. Genetic inheritance and epigenetic not even being the focal points here.

Isaiah 26:14 They are dead, they shall not live; they are deceased, they shall not rise: therefore hast thou visited and destroyed them, and made all their memory to perish.

John 5:28-29 Marvel not at this: for the hour is coming, in the which all that are in the graves shall hear his voice, and shall come forth; they that have done good, unto the resurrection of life; and they that have done evil, unto the resurrection of damnation.

Horizontal Gene Transfer is the movement of genetic information between organisms, a process that includes the spread of antibiotic resistance genes among bacteria (except for those from parent to offspring), fueling pathogen evolution. The bacteriophage is the Ancient vehicle of HGT, the chariot of the Gods!

Many resistance genes evolved long ago in natural environments with no anthropogenic influence but these genes are now rapidly spreading to and among human pathogens. HGT occurs by three well-understood genetic mechanisms:

- Transformation: Bacteria take up DNA from their environment
- Conjugation: Bacteria directly transfer genes to another cell
- Transduction: Bacteriophages (bacterial viruses) move genes from one cell to another

- National Library of Medicine

Previous studies have looked at HGT between bacteria and their viruses and have shown that it plays a major role in the movement of genes between bacterial species.

However the new study, published in Nature Microbiology, looks at interactions between viruses and eukaryotes, which include animals, plants, fungi, protists and most algae.

"We knew from individual examples that viral genes have played a role in the evolution of eukaryotes. Even humans have viral genes, which are important for our development and brain function," said the study's lead author, Dr. Nicholas Irwin, a Junior Research Fellow at Merton College, University of Oxford, and former PhD student at the University of British

Columbia (UBC). "We wanted to understand more broadly how HGT has affected viruses and eukaryotes from across the tree of life."

- University of British Columbia (January 5, 2022)

To understand the effect of particular dietary and lifestyle activities on Mental Illness read or reread Melanin vs Diabetes vol 2!!!

There is a aspect of this that may sound very conspiracy theory-ish however it must be said. Understanding the finer nuances of HGT and real time resurrection, there could be a sanitize movement and a intentional generation of germ fear to block you from your Ancestral Memory. That could also be pure gobbledegook but your are at least made aware.

Lets get into the Dirt Poor vs Pay Dirt "meat & potatoes" or "Kale & Mushrooms" LOL...

Let me say this before we begin, Allergies are being discussed as the root causes of AutoImmune diseases now so they should not be taken lightly!

Qebehsenuef - God of the Intestines - means "He who purifies his brother by means of libation"

Allergies, Sensitivities and Intolerance.

In the world of health this is apart of epigenetics and apart of parenting (environment/diet control).

A large part of our children's book series is dedicated to this!!!

Go get and read or reread these books with your children! Melanin vs Diabetes Research Hip-Hop Children & Novice BioKhemistry volumes 1-6

We learn/teach in the children series about the job of the Thymus to educate the WBCs, what you need to do as a parent is make sure your child's school IS NOT LOW BUDGET! If your child's Thymus is not properly equipped it can not do a good job of educating the WBCs leading to predisposition to allergies and autoimmune diseases.

<u>SIRTUIN BOOST FOX PROTEINS WHICH TRAIN TCELLS... LIKE SPECIAL TUTORS</u>

NAD (Fructose inhibits NAD the star of the Enqi Cycle) BOOST SIRTUIN FUNCTION!

KEY NUTRIENTS: ASTRAGALUS, VITAMIN A, D, C,
B VITAMINS, CALCIUM, IRON, ZINC, SELENIUM,
MAGNESIUM, COPPER, *PHOSPHORUS

KEY PIGMENTS: PHYCOERYTHRIN, Chlorophyll,
Phycocyanin and Phycocyanobilin, Antheraxanthin,
Cryptoxanthin, Lutein, Violaxanthin, and Zeaxanthin

POLYGONUM MULTIFLORUM (IN PURPLE PHAZE)

*THYMULIN - ZINC BASED ENZYME,
THYMOPOITEN, THYMOSINS, INSULIN

Anti Islet - Receptors, Anti Gad - Gad, Anti Insulin - Vesicle/Insulin

Food Allergies - (immediate reactions) IG E

Food Intolerance - Lack of particular Enzymes

Food Sensitivities (delayed allergic reactions) - IG G & IG A

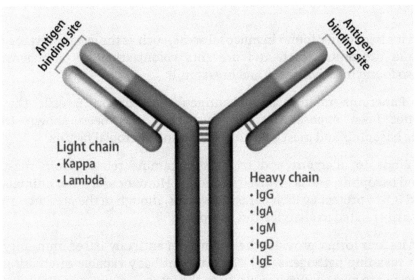

Antibodies are heavy (~150 kDa) proteins of about 10 nm in size,[17] arranged in three globular regions that roughly form a Y shape.

In humans and most other mammals, an antibody unit consists of four polypeptide chains; two identical *heavy chains* and two identical *light chains* connected by disulfide bonds.[18] Each chain is a series of domains: somewhat similar sequences of about 110 amino acids each. These domains are usually represented in simplified schematics as rectangles. Light chains consist of one variable domain V_L and one constant domain C_L, while heavy chains contain one variable domain V_H and three to four constant domains C_H1, C_H2, ...[19]

Structurally an antibody is also partitioned into two antigen-binding fragments (Fab), containing one V_L, V_H, C_L, and C_H1 domain each, as well as the crystallisable fragment (Fc), forming the trunk of the Y shape.[20] In between them is a hinge region of the heavy chains, whose flexibility allows antibodies to bind to pairs of epitopes at various distances, to form complexes (dimers, trimers, etc.), and to bind effector molecules more easily.[21]

In an electrophoresis test of blood proteins, antibodies mostly migrate to the last, gamma globulin fraction. Conversely, most gamma-globulins are antibodies, which is why the two terms were historically used as synonyms, as were the symbols Ig and γ. This variant terminology fell out of use due to the correspondence being inexact and due to confusion with γ (gamma) heavy chains which characterize the IgG class of antibodies.

Antibodies can come in different varieties known as *isotypes* or *classes*. In humans there are five antibody classes known as IgA, IgD, IgE, IgG, and IgM, which are further subdivided into subclasses such as IgA1, IgA2. The prefix "Ig" stands for *immunoglobulin*, while the suffix denotes the type of heavy chain the antibody contains: the heavy chain types α (alpha), γ (gamma), δ (delta), ε (epsilon), μ (mu) give rise to IgA, IgG, IgD, IgE, IgM, respectively. The distinctive features of each class are determined by the part of the heavy chain within the hinge and Fc region.[3]

The classes differ in their biological properties, functional locations and ability to deal with different antigens, as depicted in the table.[18] For example, IgE antibodies are responsible for an allergic response consisting of histamine release from mast cells, often a sole contributor to asthma (though other pathways exist as do exist symptoms very similar to yet not technically asthma). The antibody's variable region binds to allergic antigen, for example house dust mite particles, while its Fc region (in the ε heavy chains) binds to Fc receptor ε on a mast cell, triggering its degranulation: the release of molecules stored in its

47

granules.

IgA - In it's two forms, found in mucosal areas, such as the gut, respiratory tract and urogenital tract, and prevents colonization by pathogens. [40] Also found in saliva, tears, and breast milk.

IgD - Functions mainly as an antigen receptor on B cells that have not been exposed to antigens.[41] It has been shown to activate basophils and mast cells to produce antimicrobial factors.

IgE - Binds to allergens and triggers histamine release from mast cells and basophils, and is involved in allergy. Humans and other animals evolved IgE to protect against parasitic worms, though in the present, IgE is primarily related to allergies and asthma.

IgG - In its four forms, provides the majority of antibody-based immunity against invading pathogens.[43] The only antibody capable of crossing the placenta to give passive immunity to the fetus.

IgM - Expressed on the surface of B cells (monomer) and in a secreted form (pentamer) with very high avidity. Eliminates pathogens in the early stages of B cell-mediated (humoral) immunity before there is sufficient IgG.

HLA System - Human leukocyte antigens (HLA) are genes in major histocompatibility complexes (MHC) that help code for proteins that differentiate between self and non-self.

Spirochete Infections - (order Spirochaetales), any of a group of spiral-shaped bacteria, some of which are serious pathogens for humans, causing diseases such as syphilis, yaws, Lyme disease, and relapsing fever. Examples of genera of spirochetes include Spirochaeta, Treponema, Borrelia, and Leptospira.

Many food issues stem from being Polar or Equatorial haplotypes ie Celiac Disease. Celiac Disease or Wheat Allergy is largely a Polar issue simply because historically this was not a staple food source, where as Milk Intolerance is largely a Equatorial issue because animal fat & animal flesh were not staple foods. Spirochete infections can present similar symptoms which is why regardless of your course of action you have planned, YOU SHOULD ALWAYS GO TO THE DOCTOR AND GET DIAGNOSED.

Below I am going to include the Abstract from Alessio Fasano's article which is praised as ground breaking research. My problem with this is over 20 years prior Dr. Sebi was describing this phenomena and did not get critical acclaim, in fact his work has been plagiarized by many and he was called a Pseudo Scientist and a Quack. The only acceptable frame of reference for a leaky gut was Celiac Disease and anal sex or food as a cause sounded completely alien.

It is important for us to remember his work and the work of all of our geniuses that WESTERN ACADEMIA IGNORES! At any rate this guy Alessio is credited as the first person to bring the concept of "Leaky Gut" to the masses...

All disease begins in the (leaky) gut: role of zonulin-mediated gut permeability in the pathogenesis of some chronic inflammatory diseases

Alessio Fasano, Conceptualization, Data Curation, Formal Analysis, Funding Acquisition, Investigation, Resources, Visualization, Writing – Original Draft Preparationa,1,2
Author information Article notes Copyright and License information PMC Disclaimer

Go to:

Abstract

Improved hygiene leading to reduced exposure to microorganisms has been implicated as one possible cause for the recent "epidemic" of chronic inflammatory diseases (CIDs) in industrialized countries. That is the essence of the hygiene hypothesis that argues that rising incidence of CIDs may be, at least in part, the result of lifestyle and environmental changes that have made us too "clean" for our own good, so causing changes in our microbiota. Apart from genetic makeup and exposure to environmental triggers, inappropriate increase in intestinal permeability (which may be influenced by the composition of the gut microbiota), a "hyper-belligerent" immune system responsible for the tolerance–immune response balance, and the composition of gut microbiome and its epigenetic influence on the host genomic expression have been identified as three additional elements in causing CIDs. During the past decade, a growing number of publications have focused on human genetics, the gut microbiome, and proteomics, suggesting that loss of mucosal barrier function, particularly in the gastrointestinal tract, may substantially affect antigen trafficking, ultimately influencing the close bidirectional interaction between gut microbiome and our immune system. This cross-talk is highly influential in shaping the host gut immune system function and ultimately shifting genetic predisposition to clinical outcome. This observation led to a re-visitation of the possible causes of CIDs epidemics, suggesting a key pathogenic role of gut permeability. Pre-clinical and clinical studies have shown that the zonulin family, a group of proteins modulating gut permeability, is implicated in a variety of CIDs, including autoimmune, infective, metabolic, and tumoral diseases. These data offer novel therapeutic targets for a variety of CIDs in which the zonulin pathway is implicated in their pathogenesis.

In the same way as Alzheimer's thats decades to develop many Autoiummne diseases take 3-10 years to develop in many instances, beginning with Allergies. The solution is to be dirty. DO NOT OVERLY SANITIZE YOUR LIFE! Hand sanitizing your children in my opinion is a no no. I have not gone to medical school but I have raised 10 children! I raised 5 of that 10 through the Coranivus Pandemic and I did this alone. Just them and I.

Studies show that children that live either in poverty or on farms have a much stronger immune system and a much more diverse microbiome. In many instances a lot of what we call our immune system is our microbiome. Our microbiome produces nutrients that are crucial to our health and keep in mind that the #1 or #2 cause of bankruptcy is always medical bills. Thiamine, folate, biotin, riboflavin, and panthothenic acid are water-soluble vitamins that are plentiful in the diet, but that are also synthesized by gut bacteria. Likewise, it has been estimated that up to half of the daily Vitamin K requirement is provided by gut bacteria.

Molecular analysis of the microbiota of lean and obese mice demonstrated that the obese microbiome is markedly enriched in genes enabling breakdown of dietary polysaccharides, e.g., glucosidases, galactosidases, and amylases, and genes encoding proteins that transport and metabolize the products of polysaccharide metabolism. Biochemical and bomb calorimetry analyses in the same experiments demonstrated increased concentrations of SCFA's (indicating a higher degree of bacterial fermentation) and significantly less energy remaining in the feces of obese mice relative to their lean counterparts.

Short-chain fatty acids (SCFAs), the end products of fermentation of dietary fibers by the anaerobic intestinal microbiota.

The Role of Gut Microbiota in the Skeletal Muscle Development and Fat Deposition in Pigs

Qi Han,1 Xingguo Huang,1 Fuyong Yan,2,* Jie Yin,1 and Yingping Xiao3,*

In general, muscle growth and development are governed by multiple factors, such as **breed, genotype, sex, diet, muscle location, hormones, exercise, and ambient temperature**. Interestingly, recent studies have suggested that stable and diverse gut microbiota can govern muscle development, growth, and function. In general, muscle fiber is divided into types, namely type I or slow-oxidative, type IIA or fast oxidative-glycolytic, and fast glycolytic IIX or IIB, which are encoded by MYH7, MYH2, MYH1, and MYH4 genes, respectively. Short-chain fatty acids (SCFAs) (principally acetate, propionate, and butyrate) are gut-derived metabolites produced by anaerobic microbes through fermentation of indigestible dietary fiber in the host [30]. These SCFAs facilitate glucose uptake and promote glycogen synthesis in skeletal muscle. Studies in vitro showed that acetate or propionate administration can enhance insulin-independent glucose uptake in L6 or C2C12 myotubes, respectively [31,32]. Furthermore, emerging studies of various murine models have suggested that acetate also contributes to glycogen synthesis by inhibiting glycolysis and reducing the consequent accumulation of glucose 6-phosphate [33,34,35]. In addition, acetate treatment increased skeletal muscle Glut4 mRNA and protein levels in L6 myotubes and rats [31,36]. Importantly, Glut4, a primary glucose transporter protein, exerts an essential role in glucose uptake and metabolism into skeletal muscle [37]. Therefore, the glucose metabolism-related effects of SCFAs might be due to the Glut4 expression. - You can go find that article for more detail just remember it's based on pigs and rodents.

The purpose of the previous excerpts is to highlight that WE DO NOT KNOW EVERYTHING! There are many trainers that think they know everything there is to know about building muscle.

The new steroids will not be steroids at all. The future of steroids will be BACTERIA SUPPLEMENTS! This is one of the primary purposes of the particular Vegan Probiotic we have on **AmericanHealer.Website**

Ambient Temperature, Genotype, Sex, Diet, Muscle Location, Exercise.

*Pets help!

Ambient Temperature is as environmental as you can get, this can explain type 2 fast twitch muscle genotypes.

The C3 equatorial diet can explain the particular differences in MicroBIome that are supposed to accompany the differences in muscle tissue. The is just another of many reasons you need to **Eat Right 4 Yeur Haplotype**!

A highly Processed Diet turns your Microbiome rancid.

Eating the diet of opposite microbiome will simply change your microbiome, the problem is it won't change your genetics. You will have the right microbiome for the wrong body.

Your Microbiome must be coupled with your mitochondria, coupled with your muscle fiber types & ratio, your respiration rate etc...

Genesis 2:7 And the Lord God formed man of the **dust** of the ground, and breathed into his nostrils the breath of life; and man became a living soul. Within the dust of the ground is bacteria. The single cell organisms that DOMINATE the earth.

Genesis 2:7 And the Lord God formed man of the **dust** of the ground, and breathed into his nostrils the breath of life; and man became a living soul.

Its also the recipe, we forgot to keep the pre-commandments, commandments. The green plants, their light, the natural light. The dust of the ground is the mineral elements, the pigments (retinoid, fulvic, humic acids etc) and THE BACTERIA!

YOU KNOW HAVE IN YOUR HANDS WITH THIS BOOK, THE SCIENTIFIC ARTICLE THAT TELLS YOU WHAT THEY ATE IN ANCIENT EGYPT! That is reflective of what everyone ate at that latitude! Everyone at that latitude ate similar, live in similar ambient temperature etc...

In fact with the complete series you have your entire genetic history and blueprint, respectfully we have some things to fill in but...

The solution to allergies is easiest in the 3rd trimester of a baby's development and the first 6 months of a baby's life. The genetic development starts 24-12 months prior to conception so PLANNED PREGNANCY IS ALWAYS BEST. Doing pills, smoking blunts, drinking liquor, eating fast food etc... Is not what you want to put into your child. The most backwards thing on earth is the attention financial planning for child gets, only to have ill formed babies. Even worse is to continue poverty based nutrition after having a ill formed baby.

Powder or can baby food, creates a GMO baby! You arguing about a vaccine when your child eats fast food, was born c-section, inhales second hand smoke, was reared on fake milk etc... STOP IT!

EVEN A VEGAN OR RAW ALKALINE SO & SO, should experiment with some catfish & shrimp, I wouldn't suggest pork ever but develop your child's immune system actively. What you eat while you are pregnant is what your child eats, what you eat while you are breastfeeding is what your child eats. Just breastfeeding alone isn't it, what is in those breast?

Let them children be kids! Get it? Let them get dirty and play in the dirt, eat off the floor a little bit (I never thought I'd hear myself say that lol), seriously DO NOT OVER SANITIZE YOUR CHILD FROM FEAR. Make sure they are around other children and catching the occasional cold is good for them, it develops the Melanocytes, Langerhans, HLA, TCells and the rest of the immune systems...

Gut microbiota functions: metabolism of nutrients and other food components

Ian Rowland,[1] Glenn Gibson,[1] Almut Heinken,[2] Karen Scott,[3] Jonathan Swann,[4] Ines Thiele,[2] and Kieran Tuohy[5]

The gut microbiota makes an important contribution to human metabolism by contributing enzymes that are not encoded by the human genome, for example, the breakdown of polysaccharides, polyphenols and synthesis of vitamins. The evidence for the role of the microbiota in metabolism of dietary components and for its impact on health is derived from comparative studies in germ-free and conventional microbiota, or human microbiota-associated animals, and from in vitro studies using human faecal incubations or more complex continuous culture gut models. As such, the gut microbiota is a key factor in shaping the biochemical profile of the diet and, therefore, its impact on host health and disease. Read full article for more details.

*DO NOT WASTE YOUR LIFE, MAKE SURE YOUR GENETIC MATERIAL

IS PUT USE AFFTER YOU TRANSITION. I AM NOT TALKING ABOUT DONATING YOUR ORGANS EITHER. ALLOW YOUR BODY TO RETURN TO THE EARTH OR THE SKY! THIS DOES NOT PRECLUDE YOU FROM DONATION ORGANS BUT DO NOT DONATE YOUR WHOLE BODY.

Closing on this section, no matter what age you are it is not to late to rebuild your microbiome and your microvirome (native viruses and bacteriophages). The older you are, the more difficult it will be to get rid of allergies and will probably require a medical doctor to be on hand for each time you expose yourself and/or child to foods they are allergic to.

The cheat code is to do the research, find the particular enzymes and bacteria required to digest the very causes of your allergy, load up on them... Eat the fibers and pigments that support them, you can change your microbiome with time.

6000 YEARS AGO

In the brain there are now said to be more than 3,000 types of cells and in the body more than 400 types of cells (over 60 tisse types). The Heart and immune system has to regulate all of these cells and even the cells yet to be discovered.

Between 4 billion years ago (estimate first cells) and 500+ million years ago (estimate first complex organisms), the first immune systems began to be developed. These are basically the military and police force of your personal cellular community. In fact you are the comprised of that 4 billion years of information. You have a innate and adaptive immune system which are regulated by the pigment system. Sidebar this all fits my hypothesis, which is the 6,000ish year creation bible story is about the new consciousness or spirit... At any rate lets review some specifics...

Innate Immune System or Frontline System - Natural Killer Cells, Macrophages, Neutrophils, Dendritic Cells, Eosinophils, Mast Cells and Basophils

Adaptive Immune System or Officers/Thinking System - T & B Lymphocytes (also memory/spy cells)

Both systems of Cells are regulated by Anubis, yes Nitric Oxide! Kemetic Science is undefeated!

Nitric oxide in immunity and inflammation

J W Coleman 1
Affiliations expand

 • 		PMID: 11515807 DOI: 10.1016/s1567-5769(01)00086-8
Abstract

Nitric oxide (NO) is synthesised by many cell types involved in immunity and inflammation. The principal enzyme involved is the inducible type-2 isoform of nitric oxide synthase (NOS-2), which produces high-level sustained NO synthesis. NO is important as a toxic defense molecule against infectious organisms. It also regulates the functional activity, growth and death of many immune and inflammatory cell types including macrophages, T lymphocytes, antigen-presenting cells, mast cells, neutrophils and natural killer cells. However, the role of NO in nonspecific and specific immunity in vivo and in immunologically mediated diseases and inflammation is poorly understood. NO does not act through a receptor-its target cell specificity depends on its concentration, its chemical reactivity, the vicinity of target cells and the way that target cells are programmed to respond. At high concentrations as generated by NOS-2, NO is rapidly oxidised to reactive nitrogen oxide species (RNOS) that mediate most of the immunological effects of NOS-2-derived NO. RNOS can S-nitrosate thiols to modify key signalling molecules such as kinases and transcription factors. Several key enzymes in mitochondrial respiration are also inhibited by RNOS and this leads to a depletion of ATP and cellular energy. A combination of these interactions may explain the multiple actions of NO in the regulation of immune and inflammatory cells. T-Cells are just as intelligent as Melanocytes in some ways even more intelligent, I am in love with them! Its not the body's computer its user error. PLEASE GO READ, REREAD AND THEN REREAD AGAIN THE ALGARHYTHM!!!

Histamine is the alarm system and in my opinion we are in the process of educating the body still. Doctors will tell you that the body's cells aren't keeping up with the environmental changes however the cells are fine, the changes are synthetic. These changes are man made and our cells aren't tied to the man made items in our environment, we have to handle that ourselves. Wealth is killing us. Wealth is consuming our babies.

Allergic reactions constrict the muscles are the lungs, slowing down the breath (as mucus clogs your nasal passages) while at the same time causing vasodilation dropping blood pressure and enhancing blood flow. A recipe for death. This is just one of the ways our immune system can kill us and this happens very quickly, minutes to hours, usually 27 minutes or less.

Histamine activates, or is supposed to activate Nitric Oxide production, which is supposed to down regulate Histamine. I don't know why there isnt more talk about this natural process to stop Histamine! Adrenaline of course stops Histamine faster but epinephrine (hence epi pen) has to make it's way onto the scene. Histamine is like a lie or bad news, it spreads so fast that....

Epipens are the first-line therapy for anaphylaxis, for this reason! Immediate treatment is critical to prevent mortality.

Think about being a kid with Pollen Allergies (trees and plants are foreign to them), the things that grow on trees like nuts are foreign to them, the sun creates it's own series of inflammatory issues etc... That is a horrific life, no amount of money is worth being BROKE GENETICALLY! We are trading Pay Dirt for being Dirt Poor!!! Lack of bacteria = Dirt Poor (physically).

Cocaine and Crack ushered in the age of wealth and allergies in the 90s!

Roughly 6,000 years ago I believe that the operating system of the human computer got updated. I believe that was the start of this world we live on now. Particularly at the equator in Africa the last 3 books we have been compiling that documentation. Nutrimiromics is another way to maximize your potential wether you are from the equator or not.

I always thought Steve Jobs died trying to follow a equatorial diet, when he was ill, instead of a Polar diet like Bill Gates suggested. From the research we have it looks like the Garden of Eden is the Nile Valley. The magical science the priest and mystery schools were studying was simply chemistry. The gods that mankind (the kind of cell) was created in the image and likeness of, is simply describing the elements that make up the cell. The periodic table is the "Gods of Kemet" and manifestations of that science like todays Green Screen or Lysol....

Osiris being the perfect black but his skin is Green, we know our skin is green now. Our blood is green but our eyes can't interpret that color green. Hollywood has generated Trillions off that knowledge but never once shared it with the people in a meaningful way.

Equatorial Haplotypes are now stuck in a synthetic version of the Polar world. Our technology just like the ice and snow, reflect mostly Blue Light. Blue Light like many things is toxic to all humans but particularly toxic to brown and black people. Vitamin A is the seed for pigment, the Heart is largely a pigment based organ (so vitamin A is crucial), the Liver is similar to the Heart and most of all the Pancreas! Let me provide some examples below and keep this in mind for your children. Bad eyes is the way to know they are short on Vitamin A! That may extend to their hearts, livers and pancreas!

Liver stellate cells (HSCs; also called as vitamin A-storing cells, lipocytes, interstitial cells, fat-storing cells, Ito cells) exist in the space between parenchymal cells and sinusoidal endothelial cells of the hepatic lobule, and store 80% of vitamin A in the whole body as retinyl palmitate in lipid droplets in the cytoplasm.

Vitamin A attenuates cell receptors to Histamine, modulating sensitivity to Histamine.

Cardiac retinoic acid levels decline in heart failure

Ni Yang,[1] Lauren E. Parker,[1] Jianshi Yu,[2] Jace W. Jones,[2] Ting Liu,[1] Kyriakos N. Papanicolaou,[1] C. Conover Talbot, Jr.,[3] Kenneth B. Margulies,[4] Brian O'Rourke,[1] Maureen A. Kane,[2] and D. Brian Foster[1]
Author information Article notes Copyright and License information PMC Disclaimer

Associated Data

Supplementary Materials

Go to:

Abstract

Although low circulating levels of the vitamin A metabolite, all-*trans* retinoic acid (ATRA), are associated with increased risk of cardiovascular events and all-cause mortality, few studies have addressed whether cardiac retinoid levels are altered in the failing heart. Here, we showed that proteomic analyses of human and guinea pig heart failure (HF) were consistent with a decline in resident cardiac ATRA. Quantitation of the retinoids in ventricular myocardium by mass spectrometry revealed 32% and 39% ATRA decreases in guinea pig HF and in patients with idiopathic dilated cardiomyopathy (IDCM), respectively, despite ample reserves of cardiac vitamin A. ATRA (2 mg/kg/d) was sufficient to mitigate cardiac remodeling and prevent functional decline in guinea pig HF. Although cardiac ATRA declined in guinea pig HF and human IDCM, levels of certain retinoid metabolic enzymes diverged. Specifically, high expression of the ATRA-catabolizing enzyme, CYP26A1, in human IDCM could dampen prospects for an ATRA-based therapy. Pertinently, a pan-CYP26 inhibitor, talarozole, blunted the impact of phenylephrine on ATRA decline and hypertrophy in neonatal rat ventricular myocytes. Taken together, we submit that low cardiac ATRA attenuates the expression of critical ATRA-dependent gene programs in HF and that strategies to normalize ATRA metabolism, like CYP26 inhibition, may have therapeutic potential.

Retinoids in the pancreas

Pierre-Jacques Brun1, Nuttaporn Wongsiriroj2, William S. Blaner1

1Department of Medicine, College of Physicians and Surgeons, Columbia University, New York, NY 10032, USA; 2Institute of Molecular Biosciences, Mahidol University, Nakhon Pathom, Thailand

Contributions: (I) Conception and design: All authors; (II) Administrative support: None; (III) Provision of study materials or patients: None; (IV) Collection and assembly of data: None; (V) Data analysis and interpretation: None; (VI) Manuscript writing: All authors; (VII) Final approval of manuscript: All authors.

Correspondence to: William S. Blaner. Department of Medicine, College of Physicians and Surgeons, Columbia University, 650 W. 168th St., New York, NY 10032, USA. Email: wsb2@columbia.edu.

Abstract: Retinoids (vitamin A and its natural and synthetic analogs) are required by most tissues for maintaining the normal health of the tissue. This is certainly true for the pancreas. The recent literature is convincing that retinoids are needed by the adult to assure normal pancreatic endocrine functions, especially those of the α- and β-cells. It is also well established that retinoids are required to insure normal pancreas development in utero, including the development of the endocrine pancreas. The actions of retinoids for maintaining normal pancreatic islet functions has drawn considerable research interest from investigators interested in understanding and treating metabolic disease. Pancreatic retinoids are also of interest to investigators studying the origins of pancreatic disease, including the development of pancreatic fibrosis and its sequelae. This research interest is focused on pancreatic stellate cells (PSCs) which store retinoids and possess the metabolic machinery needed to metabolize retinoids. The literature on pancreatic disease and retinoids suggests that there is an association between impairments in pancreatic retinoid storage and metabolism and the development of pancreatic disease. These topics will be considered in this review. It is clear from many published studies that all-trans-retinoic acid and RAR signaling are needed to maintain proper insulin secretion from pancreatic β-cells. **It is also clear that retinoids also are needed to maintain β-cell mass within islets and to prevent β-cell apoptosis.** However, as can be garnered from a reading of the above text, there are a number of very important unresolved issues regarding retinoid actions in pancreatic islets and how these may influence glucose homeostasis.

THE HEART CHANGES NON-WORKING CELLS INTO SCAR TISSUE AS DO STELLATE/STAR CELLS!!! IN THE SAME WAY AS CONGESTIVE HEART FAILURE IS SYMBOLIZED BY SCAR TISSUE MANY OTHER ORGANS/GLANDS ie.. the LIVER DEAL WITH THIS SAME PROCESS WHILE EXHIBITING DIFFERENT SYMPTOMS OF DYSFUNCTION.

Activated Pancreatic Stellate Cells vs Quiescent Pancreatic Stellate Cells (this is a major site of Vitamin D action), the difference is Vitamin A Supply!

Quiescent PSCs: Interstitial Support, Immune Regulation, Inflammation Regulation, Beta Cell Progenitors

Activated PSCs: ECM Remodeling or Fibrosis, Loss of Beta Cells, Disrupt Islet Function, Help Cancer Cells Migrate & Proliferate

VITAMIN A - Al-trans-retinoic acid (ATRA) is a morphogen signaling molecule (PIGMENT FOOD), which means it is concentration dependent. STAR CELLS ARE THE ANGELS THAT DO THE CREATORS HANDY WORK!!!

The stellate cell, previously known as the Ito cell, fat-storing cell, perisinusoidal cell or lipocyte, is a major storage site for vitamin A, it can become a transitional cell or myofibroblast-like cell capable of synthesizing collagen types I, III and IV as well as laminin. In the human body, the stellate cell system consists of retinoid-storing cells in various organs, including the **liver, pancreas, lung, kidney, intestine, spleen,**

<u>adrenal gland, ductus deferens and vocal cords</u> showing a perivascular location with a distribution typical of a pericyte. THESE ARE THE CELLS THAT REGENERATE THE LIVER, PERFORM ANGIOGENESIS AND RECRUIT HEMATOPOIETIC STEM CELLS!!!

Harmine suppresses collagen production in hepatic stellate cells by inhibiting DYRK1B

It is a good idea to get plenty of Purple Haze into your diet and blend some into smoothies for the Children! You also need to pay particular attention to keeping orange, red & yellow foods in your daily diet!

*Greens are loaded with red, yellow and orange pigments, they aren't visible but they are in there! Green Powder in a smoothie with some deeply pigmented fruit, Bleu Magick & Momatomix is my go to...

Keep in mind that Vitamin A is a another Pigment! Well pigment-like substance, its kind magical!

Vitamin A Exerts a Photoprotective Action in Skin by Absorbing Ultraviolet B Radiation

Author links open overlay panel
Christophe Antille, Christian Tran, Olivier Sorg, Pierre Carraux, Liliane Didierjean, Jean-Hilaire Saurat
Show more
Add to Mendeley

Retinyl esters, a storage form of vitamin A, concentrate in the epidermis, and absorb ultraviolet radiation with a maximum at 325 nm. We wondered whether these absorbing properties of retinyl esters might have a biologically relevant filter activity. We first used an in vitro model to assess the photoprotective properties of retinyl palmitate. We then applied topical retinyl palmitate on the back of hairless mice before exposing them to 1 J per cm2 ultraviolet B, and assayed the levels of thymine dimers produced in epidermal DNA 2 h following ultraviolet B exposure. Finally, we applied topical retinyl palmitate or a sunscreen on the buttocks of human volunteers before exposing them to four minimal erythema doses of ultraviolet B; we assayed the levels of thymine dimers produced 2 h following ultraviolet B exposure, and determined the intensity of erythema 24 h after ultraviolet B. In vitro, retinyl palmitate was shown to be as efficient as the commercial filter octylmethoxycinnamate in preventing ultraviolet-induced fluorescence or photobleaching of fluorescent markers. The formation of thymine dimers in mouse epidermis was significantly inhibited by topical retinyl palmitate. In human subjects, topical retinyl palmitate was as efficient as a sun protection factor 20 sunscreen in preventing sunburn erythema as well as the formation of thymine dimers. These results demonstrate that epidermal retinyl esters have a biologically relevant filter activity and suggest, besides their pleomorphic biologic actions, a new role for vitamin A that concentrates in the epidermis.

Let's close this chapter on a **strong** note (pun intended). In Hebrew the word Qabbalah/Kabbalah has the numerical equivalent of 137.

Qabbalah/Kabbalah = 137 now in light of the fine structure constant you should know why we change the 16/8 rule to the 13/7 rule! Add the carbohydrate number science, from the Divine Mathematics Book & the AlgaRhythm Book you will be cooking with fish grease (olive oil LOL)...The number is required to know how specific wavelengths of light interact in precise ways with atoms and how electromagnetic forces hold atoms together.

ROUTINE

Muscles are highly electromagnetic fibers, and electric impulses from neurons/nerves initiated in the brain stimulate the fibers to contract (calcium) and relax (magnesium). Fast-twitch muscle fibers move rapidly for fast, high-intensity movements for short periods ie.. jumping rope, sprinting, calisthenics, jumping jacks, box jumping, weightlifting and strength-training. The hands and eyes are primarily fast twitch muscle.

The erector spinae in the lower back and soleus muscles, are primarily slow twitch. Standing, walking etc... things that need to be done for long periods of time daily.

Here is the cheat code here: The Slow Twitch muscle need more reps!!! The slow twitch need more time under tension!!! 20 minutes 3 times a week is not going to work!!! Especially is you have that dangerous type 2 fast twitch glycolytic muscle. You should make your type 1 muscle so greedy that there is no sugar left over to ferment! Keep your bod fat percentage low!

IN PLAIN ENGLISH FAT IS SLOWLY GOING TO FERMENT IN YOU!!!

HERE: In 1956, Warburg reported that cancer cells exhibit high rates of glucose uptake and lactic acid production, even in the presence of oxygen [2], with cancer cells appearing to prefer aerobic glycolysis to oxidative phosphorylation (OXPHOS). - NIH

That is literally the exact same description of your type 2 fast twitch muscle! This is the exact same description of your kids type 2 fast twitch muscle!

Dirt Poor (genetically) kids born into well to do families, middle classes and upper classes sit down all day! They eat trash all day. These mothers may be on drugs and also sit down all day (pregnant moms should work or workout). The excess fat hurts children's mental development as we outlined in detail in Melanin vs Diabetes Book Two!

This book with Melanin vs Diabetes Book Two are like Batman and Robin to be studied together!

HIGH REPS OF ANY EXERCISE IS GOOD FOR SLOW TWITCH IE 30-60 REPS, IF YOU ADD A CLOCK THAT COMBINES THE FAST TWITCH & SLOW TWITCH MUSCLE FIBERS!

Your body is actually not designed to do slow twitch vs fast twitch by the book... Natural movements combine various muscles, compound movements work best ie Calisthenics! Weights should be used to reinforce what you do with your calisthenics only but never the main form of exercise, at least not after 35 years old. Remember the riddle of the sphinx...

In less than 5 minutes you can do toe raises, squats, knee lifts and pushups to move the blood around, lymph around and burn the sugar. 60 second sets...

There is too many articles on the benefits of exercise on Allergies, combined with what you have in Melanin vs Diabetes Book Two, you have a great blueprint for your **child** to to be a **Pay Dirt Kid**. Grades, behavior, mental illness, ADD etc...

Get out there with the children, run, walk and exercise with them! Get dirty with them you can experience the Farmhouse Effect of dirt and animals anywhere. You see I have a dog and two turtles! I keep my dog in the house, I think she helped us during the pandemic! I take Anubis seriously, you should too! Go outside and throw the football to your sons, play ball in the park. Each time the basketball hits the ground and then your hand its getting dirty. We have to begin appreciating the dirt, forget hugging a tree, no don't forget to hug trees but don't forget to sit or sleep under them. Jump rope with your daughters, play on the slide with them! The sliding boards and monkey bars are filthy, the public swings are filthy, enjoy them!

Don't hide from germs. You are made from germs.

If you don't have children exercise daily in a near by park, join a outdoor sports team.

Boost Grades, Improve Behavior

Teachers can help improve test scores and student behavior by incorporating physical activity breaks into their daily classroom routines.

Research has shown that students who do brief bursts of exercise before taking tests score higher. In addition, regular activity breaks during the school day can help sharpen students' abilities to focus and stay on task.

Before trying these exercises in your classroom, make sure none of your students have health conditions that require restrictions on physical activity. Make sure each student has plenty of space, and won't bump into classmates or anything else in your room.

Also check to see if all your students are wearing appropriate shoes, such as sneakers. If students touch the floor during any exercises, make sure they wash their hands with soap and water or hand sanitizer when they're done their exercise break.

When taking a break, encourage activities that get the body moving and the heart pumping, such as dancing, jumping, and running in place. You also can try some of these easy-to-do exercises that work on flexibility, strength, and cardio. Each of these fun exercises for K-5 students takes 2-3 minutes, and kids can do them right at their desks. No equipment is needed.

Start with a brief warm-up (like jumping jacks or jogging in place) before performing these exercises.

Light Exercises

Kids doing light physical exercises breathe normally as they do basic gross motor activities at a controlled pace.

Sky reaches

Do this three times:

- Stand up.

- Swing arms up to the sky.

- Rise up on your tippy toes.

- Reach for the sky while keeping your body tight.

- Hold for 15 seconds.

- Lower your heels and arms.

Shoulder blasts

Do this 10 times:

- Hold your arms straight out to the sides.

- Make arm circles forward (start with small circles, then gradually larger circles).

- Reverse direction and make arm circles backward (large circles, then gradually smaller circles).

- Raise your arms in front of your body and move your arms up and down.

- Raise your arm above your head and wave them side to side, like a windshield wiper.

- Pump your arms above head to "raise the roof."

Squats

Do this 10 times slowly:

- Stand with your legs a little wider than shoulder-width apart.

- Hold your arms out in front of your body.

- Slowly bend your knees and squat down until your thighs are parallel to the floor.

- Rise up slowly.

Hand walks

Do this five times:

- Bend forward at your waist.

- Reach down and touch hands to floor.

- Walk your hands out for a count of 8.

- Walk your hands to left for a count of 4.

- Walk your hands back to the center for a count of 4.

- Walk your hands right for a count of 4.

- Walk your hands back to the center for a count of 4.

- Walk your hands back for a count of 8.

Star jumps

Do this 10 times:

- Squat until your thighs are parallel to the floor (see squats).

- From this position, jump up reaching your hands and feet out like a star.

- Land softly on your feet, dropping back to the squat position.

Mountain climbers

Do 20 foot switches:

- On the floor, go to a plank position by putting your:
  - Hands flat on the floor
  - Hands shoulder-width apart
  - Arms straight
  - Back flat
- Mimic a running motion by switching one foot at a time.

Students can add intensity by adding speed.

Moderate Exercises

Kids doing moderate physical exercises breathe harder than normal, move fairly quickly, and find it a little difficult to talk during the activities.

Sun salutation

Do this dynamic yoga stretch five times:

- Start with your feet together, hands at your side, and your head in a neutral position.

- Raise your arms out to the side and overhead.

- Bend forward at your waist and put your hands on the floor.

- Step or jump your feet back to the plank position (see mountain climbers).

- Do half of a push-up (can drop to the knees).

- Drop your hips toward the floor, lift head and chest into an "up-dog," and hold for 5 seconds.

- Lift your hips and drop your head and shoulders to a "down-dog," and hold for 5 seconds.

- Step or jump your feet back toward your hands in a forward bend.

- Rise slowly to a standing position.

Moving through positions more quickly will increase the cardio workout.

To enhance stretching and strength, kids can hold forward bends and the up- and down-dogs for longer than 5 seconds.

Robots

Do this fast exercise 20 times:

- Stand up tall.

- Hop forward, then immediately backward.

- At the same time, raise one arm up and one arm down.

- Keep hopping your feet front and back while alternating arms up and down simultaneously.

Hand pushes

Do this isometric exercise, five times, with a 20-second break between each:

- Put your hands in front of your face, with your palms touching.

- Push your palms and fingers against themselves.

- Keep pushing your hands together for 10-15 seconds.

Students can push their hands together as hard as they are comfortable as long as it doesn't hurt. Make sure students breathe during this exercise, because many kids tend to hold their breath while pushing. Challenge students to stand on one leg while pushing, then repeat standing on other leg.

Frog jumps

Do this dynamic exercise 12 times:

- Start in the squat position (see squats), feet a little wider than shoulder-width apart.

- Put your hands between your legs, like a frog.

- Jump upward, and softly land back to the frog position.

Students may want to try this variation: While jumping up, click your heels together.

Vigorous Exercises

Kids doing vigorous physical exercises breathe much harder than normal, move quite fast, and find talking to be difficult and labored during the activities.

Jump lunges

Do this 12 times slowly, making sure to stay balanced:

- Stand tall with your feet together.

- Place your hands on your hips or hold your arms out straight for balance.

- Move into a lunge position by stepping one foot forward and bending your knee (don't extend your knee past your toes).

- Hop and switch your feet so that your back foot comes forward to a bent-knee position, while the other foot goes back.

With this exercise, form is more important than speed.

Desk push-ups

Do this 12 times:

- Put your hands firmly on the edge of your desk.

- Step your feet back so you're leaning into your desk.

- Bend your elbows and slowly lower your body toward your desk, keeping your back straight.

- Push yourself away from your desk.

Make sure desks are stable and feet don't slip on floor. To increase difficulty, students can move their feet back farther from their desks or move their hands closer together on their desks.

T push-ups

Do this 10 times slowly:

- On the floor, start in the plank position (see mountain climbers).

- Lift one arm up and turn your body sideways so that your body looks like the letter T.

- Hold the T for 5 seconds.

- Return to the plank position, then repeat with your other side.

Burpees

Do this 10 times:

- Stand tall with your hands at your side.

- Squat down to the floor (see squats).

- Put your hands on the floor.

- Jump to the plank position (see mountain climbers).

- Jump your feet back to the squat position.

- Star jump back up (see star jumps).

Medically reviewed by: Mary L. Gavin, MD - kidshealth.org

LISTEN I HAVE MULTIPLE AIR FILTERS AND WATER FILTERS, DON'T GET IT TWISTED. THERE IS A DIFFERNCE BETWEEN PATHOGEN FREE AND GERM!

BRAIN

Cerebrospinal fluid physiology: visualization of cerebrospinal fluid dynamics using the magnetic resonance imaging Time-Spatial Inversion Pulse method

Shinya Yamada

Author information Article notes Copyright and License information PMC Disclaimer

Go to:

Abstract

Previously there have been no methods for directly tracing the flow of cerebrospinal fluid (CSF) under physiological conditions, and the circulation of CSF has therefore been studied and visualized by injecting a radioactively labeled tracer or contrast medium visible in x-ray images. The newly developed Time-Spatial Inversion Pulse (Time-SLIP) method makes it possible **to directly visualize the flow of CSF using magnetic resonance imaging** (MRI), permitting CSF dynamics to be depicted in a certain time frame. The **CSF dynamics** visualized using Time-SLIP **has been found to differ markedly from the classical CSF circulation theory described in medical textbooks**. It can be said that research on CSF dynamics has advanced to the next stage with the use of this innovative imaging method. Obtaining a more accurate understanding of normal CSF physiology and pathophysiology should lead to improved diagnostic accuracy, permit the identification of new etiological factors in a variety of diseases, and promote the development of new therapeutic approaches.

Descriptions of the physiological circulatory dynamics of cerebrospinal fluid (CSF) can be found mainly in neurosurgery textbooks. More than a hundred years ago, it was only natural that the circulation of CSF was considered to be similar to the circulation of blood. It was naturally thought that the physiology of CSF followed the same pattern as that of blood, which is a typical example of a physiological phenomenon in the body. Harvey Cushing, who was a pioneer in the field of neurosurgery, referred to the CSF as the third circulation (1,2). Since there were previously no methods for directly observing the flow of CSF under physiological conditions, the circulation of CSF has been studied and visualized in humans by injecting a radioactively labeled tracer or contrast medium visible in x-ray images. A needle was inserted into the cerebrospinal space and the observed flow was assumed to reflect that of the CSF. Given this background, the ability to visualize the flow of CSF within a single heartbeat using the phase contrast technique in magnetic resonance imaging (MRI) without the need to inject a tracer into the cerebrospinal space was truly revolutionary. Although considerable research has been conducted using this approach (3-7), it is unfortunately not routinely employed in the clinical setting today. This is because the information obtained using the phase contrast technique is insufficient for making definitive clinical judgments.

Although the newly developed Time-Spatial Inversion Pulse (Time-SLIP) method makes it possible to visualize the flow of CSF using MRI, the imaging procedures and examination time are fundamentally different from those of the phase contrast technique. Therefore, most of the information obtained using these methods cannot be directly compared with each other. In the Time-SLIP method, the CSF itself serves as an endogenous tracer when radiofrequency (RF) pulses are applied. The flow of CSF can be observed for a period of approximately 5 seconds until the effects of the RF pulses diminish and are no longer visible. The Time-SLIP method makes it possible to depict CSF dynamics in a time frame that is not possible with any other method.

The CSF dynamics visualized using Time-SLIP differ markedly from the descriptions of CSF flow that have been given in medical textbooks. **CSF is clear like water in the absence of diseases such as meningitis, and it has been demonstrated that it undergoes turnover.** However, whether or not the CSF flows like a river from the sites where it is produced to the sites where it is absorbed requires further verification (8,9).

Go to:

Visualization of CSF dynamics using MRI with the Time-SLIP method

A detailed explanation of the principles of Time-SLIP can be found in other reports (10). Briefly, since the CSF itself is marked with RF pulses in MRI, the dynamics of the CSF can be visualized as long as this marking persists. It takes about 8 seconds for signals of marked water to return to their original levels in a 1.5-tesla magnetic field. However, the practical observation time is considered to be just under 5 to 6 seconds, since visualization is based on the contrast between the marked CSF and background area. In the Time-SLIP method, a non-selective inversion recovery (IR) pulse is applied to the entire field of view, a selective inversion pulse is applied to the region to be examined, and images are then acquired after a specified delay time (**Figure 1**). The delay time for image acquisition can be adjusted to acquire images at different timings. The images can be acquired one by one and then arranged in sequence on the time axis or can be acquired as fully sequential images. Images acquired using the former method tend to be of higher quality in terms of resolution. However, due to the principles of this method, the continuity of the images is lost when they are displayed as a movie in the situation when there is more than one force driving CSF (11).

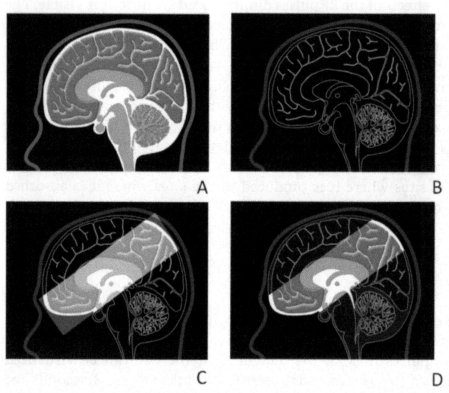

Figure 1

Illustration of the Time-Spatial Inversion Pulse (Time-SLIP) sequence. A non-selective inversion recovery pulse inverts all signals in the field of view from initial longitudinal magnetization (+Mz) to (–Mz) (**A**). Immediately after the initial inversion, a second spatially selective inversion pulse is applied to invert (tag) only the magnetization in the region of interest (white rectangle) (**B**). The magnetization in the marked region is restored to (+Mz), whereas the magnetization elsewhere is (–Mz) (**C**). Images are obtained after a specified period of time. The tagged cerebrospinal fluid (CSF) that has moved into the non-tagged background area produces contrast between the tagged and untagged CSF, which can be visualized during the time period of 1000-5000 ms (arrow) (**D**). Supplementary video 1.

The fact that CSF motion varies in response to cardiac pulsation and respiratory motion can be observed as a fluid level fluctuation in the ventricular external drainage tube from the patient cerebral ventricle, observing the changes in fluid level of the CSF during surgery and the lumbar puncture. In other words, CSF dynamics exhibit various types of motion according to the combination of cardiac pulsation and respiratory motion, which means that the data must be acquired in real time (11). This driving force is also an issue in the phase contrast technique. In the conventional phase contrast technique, images are acquired by adding and averaging images for many cardiac cycles using the cardiac pulsation as a trigger, and the motion of CSF attributable to respiratory motion is not taken into consideration (5,7). During surgery and in scans with Time-SLIP, the flow of CSF attributable to respiratory motion is observed, and it has been found to have a greater effect than the flow attributable to cardiac pulsation (11). Considering this point, the variation among data sets measured using the phase contrast technique, which has been assumed to be a problem, may in fact be due to the CSF motion attributable to respiratory motion. Image acquisition in the phase contrast technique usually takes about 2 to 3 minutes. It is important not only to look at the results, but also to understand the principles of the technique and the process by which the results are obtained.

Go to:

Physiological CSF dynamics in the ventricular system

Using Time-SLIP, the flow of CSF from the third ventricle into the lateral ventricles has been observed (Figure 2). **CSF flow into the lateral ventricles is seen when RF pulses are applied to the CSF in the third ventricle (a process referred to as tagging). Since the flow of CSF had previously been assumed to be from the lateral ventricles to the third ventricle based on the descriptions in medical textbooks, it took some time to understand this finding. This flow is opposite to the conventional concept of CSF physiology and can be described as a backflow into the lateral ventricles.**

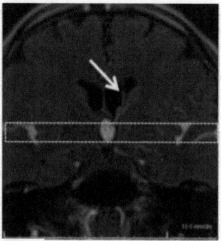

Figure 2
The flow of cerebrospinal fluid (CSF) into the lateral ventricles is depicted (arrow) when radiofrequency (RF) pulses are applied to the CSF in the third ventricle (dotted rectangle) in this coronal view of the normal brain. Supplementary video 2.

Actually, it was previously thought that this type of CSF flow does not occur in healthy persons (12), but only in patients with hydrocephalus, who have impaired CSF circulation (13-15). This was based on the finding that when contrast medium or radioisotope (RI) is injected into the CSF in the lumbar subarachnoid space in patients with hydrocephalus, the CSF is seen to flow back into the lateral ventricles. This finding, which is called ventricular reflux of the CSF, has been used to confirm the diagnosis of hydrocephalus (13-15) (Figure 3A).

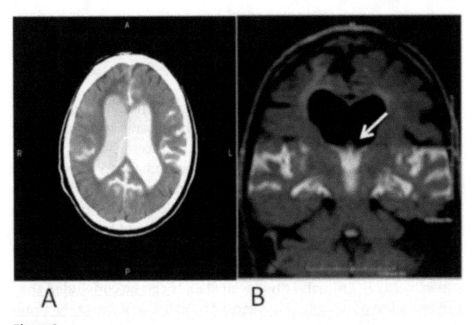

Figure 3
Patient with communicating hydrocephalus. Metrizamide CT cisternography indicates ventricular reflux (black arrow) (**A**). However, cerebrospinal fluid (CSF) flow into the lateral ventricles from the third ventricle is not observed using the Time-SLIP method (white arrow) in the hydrocephalic brain (**B**). Supplementary video 3.

When we consider this finding more deeply, it is clear that we are unable to answer the simple question "Where is the CSF produced in the case of hydrocephalus in which ventricular reflux is observed?" Nevertheless, this theory was widely accepted as the truth for nearly 50 years until CSF dynamics could be clearly visualized using Time-SLIP. No CSF reflux from the third ventricle to the lateral ventricles was observed in a patient with hydrocephalus using Time-SLIP MR imaging (**Figure 3B**). Since stagnation of the CSF occurs due to impaired CSF circulation in patients with hydrocephalus, a tracer such as contrast medium or RI reaches the lateral ventricles by the mixing and diffusion that accompanies the agitation after the injection into the lumbar subarachnoid space. We can now appreciate that what is actually observed is this phenomenon. In other words, it can be said that these exogenous tracer studies (13-15) are able to demonstrate the presence of communication between the site of injection and the final destination, but it cannot be said that such studies are able to trace the bulk flow of CSF.

The CSF motion visualized using Time-SLIP does not show unidirectional backflow of CSF into the lateral ventricles, but rather demonstrates that the CSF in the lateral ventricles and the CSF in the third ventricle are actively exchanged through the foramen of Monro in the normal brain. On the other hand, there is virtually no flow (or only extremely slow flow) of CSF in the body of the lateral ventricles, except in the area adjacent to the foramen of Monro (**Figure 4**). At least in humans, the steady state flow from posterior to anterior observed in recent exogenous tracer experiments in animals is not seen (16). **It can be concluded that the injection of exogenous tracers is unable to accurately show the flow of CSF and that the CSF flow observed is obviously artificially induced flow.**

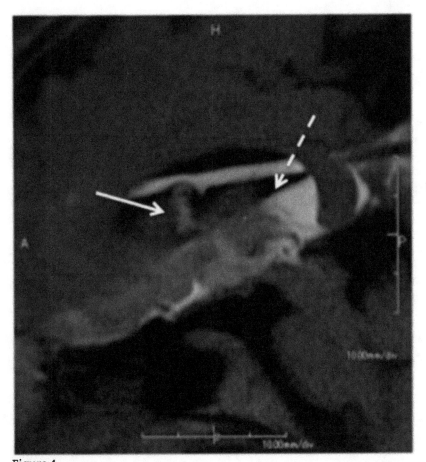

Figure 4
Sagittal oblique view of the normal brain. Pulsatile motion through the aqueduct is observed. Cerebrospinal fluid (CSF) reflux from the third ventricle to the lateral ventricle is also observed. However, no CSF motion is seen in the body of lateral ventricle (dotted arrow). Supplementary video 4.

In examinees who are unable to remain still and therefore move their heads during MRI scanning, the CSF in the body of the lateral ventricles is strongly agitated (**Figure 5**). Considering this point in greater detail, it should also be noted that almost all previous research on CSF physiology was limited to observation of the CSF in anesthetized animals or examinees who remained still during MRI scanning. However, since people and animals do not remain still all day long, the motion of CSF that is induced by walking, sitting, or running should be considered to more accurately reflect true physiological conditions.

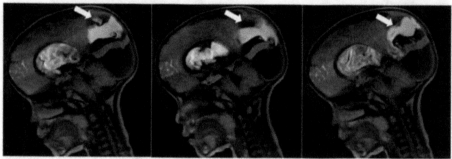

Figure 5

Seven-year-old boy who presented with ventriculomegaly associated with aqueductal stenosis. He moved his head during the scan. The cerebrospinal fluid (CSF) in the body of the lateral ventricle was agitated by head movement (arrows). Supplementary video 5.

The circulation of CSF is clearly not like that of blood, which flows through tubular blood vessels at high speed. A more accurate model may be that of placing the brain and spinal cord in a glass container, immersing them in water, and then shaking the container. Even though CSF motion can only be visualized in real time for a period of several seconds, it is clear that these observations are totally different from the classical concept of CSF circulation.

Go to:

Possible paracrine functions mediated by the CSF in the ventricular system

CSF motion in the third and fourth ventricles is swirling vortex-type flow even when the head is stationary (Figure 6). The area around the third ventricle contains a dense arrangement of vital structures that are related to the circadian rhythm. **It has recently become possible to directly observe the inner surface of the ventricles by opening a small hole in the brain and inserting an endoscope** (17). Due to remarkable improvements in spatial resolution, the visualization capabilities are completely different from those in the past. It is now possible to insert an endoscope into the third ventricle by advancing it from the lateral ventricle through the foramen of Monro after opening a small hole in the brain. We can see capillaries running from the pituitary gland in the anterior direction. Exposed red-colored blood vessels can be seen in the wall of the third ventricle. Although this may be a rather unfamiliar concept, a new theory of volume transmission involving hormonal transmitters (eg, orexin, prostaglandin D) has been proposed in contrast to the so-called neurotransmission in the form of synaptic transmission (18-21). This involves hormonal transmission, which functions in a manner similar to internal secretion in the blood. Volume transmission is thought to transmit signals to surrounding tissues by means of hormonal transmitters (ie, paracrine system in the central nervous system). **The mechanism by which the CSF transports hormonal transmitters and allows their interaction via the CSF is referred to as CSF signaling (20). This mechanism transmits signals over a considerable distance, for example from the pineal body to the pituitary gland. The turbulence and swirling CSF flow in the third ventricle (10), should have some functional significance in terms of CSF signaling, which can be referred to as the CSF paracrine system.**

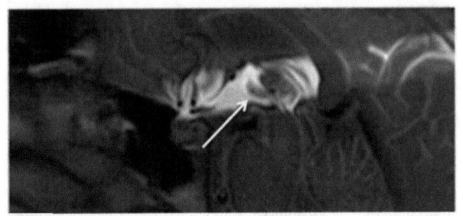

Figure 6
Midsagittal view of a normal volunteer showing turbulent cerebrospinal fluid flow in the third ventricle with the head stationary (arrow). Supplementary video 6.

We can easily imagine that the function of the CSF is surely not only to protect the brain from external forces (because the weight of the brain itself is offset as a result of being suspended in water, in accordance with Archimedes 'principle) or to serve as a means for eliminating wastes from the brain (22-26) although this may not be the textbook explanation in the field of CSF physiology. Here, it is a means for disposing of waste matter from the brain.

Go to:

Are the arachnoid villi a major site of CSF absorption in humans?

The standard method for determining the amount of CSF is based on an ingenious ventriculo-cisternal perfusion experiment described by Pappenheimer et al (27,28). Artificial CSF containing a known concentration of a substance is injected and then collected after dilution. The total amount of CSF can be calculated from the concentration of the substance in the collected fluid. Currently, CSF production levels in humans and animals are measured using this method (27,29-33). However, if you carefully check the calculation formula (27), you can see that it is based on the assumption that the CSF in the ventricular system is not absorbed by brain tissue. With the exception of some studies (8,9,34,35), most studies on CSF physiology have not considered the relationships with brain interstitial fluid.

Brain interstitial fluid has the same composition as CSF, and there is no barrier between them like the blood-brain barrier. Normally, free exchange occurs between the CSF and brain interstitial fluid (35,36) through the Virchow-Robin spaces (ie, perivascular spaces) (34,37,38), which pose the least resistance to flow. Although the blood-brain barrier is known to have diverse and complex functions that enable selective passage of high-molecular weight substances, water itself freely passes through the blood-brain barrier. Hence, it can be concluded that at least a portion of the CSF is composed of water that has passed through the blood-brain barrier (8,9,39).

According to medical textbooks, the CSF is produced by the choroid plexus. But this raises an important question: When the cerebral aqueduct or the outlets of the fourth ventricle are obstructed, where is the CSF downstream from the point of occlusion produced? This is another example of a situation in which the CSF physiology described in current medical textbooks is unable to fully explain CSF flow under physiological or pathological conditions.

At present, Time-SLIP is unable to depict the correlated dynamics of the CSF and brain interstitial fluid. Although this may be a bit of a digression from the main topic, which is the visualization of CSF using Time-SLIP, the production and absorption of CSF mediated by brain capillaries is one of the most important issues in the reassessment of CSF physiology (9,39). This has been pointed out as a matter of fact since the very early stages of CSF research, and some studies have been conducted since that time (12,39-43). However, the importance of this absorption pathway of CSF is still not adequately conveyed in standard medical textbooks, also CSF drainage from central nervous system occurs via the lymphatic system (38,44-47). It is clear that there are still many questions regarding the absorption pathways of CSF.

Time-SLIP allows the dynamics of CSF to be depicted under the most physiological conditions because it does not require the injection of a tracer. The CSF itself serves as an endogenous tracer. The most important finding related to the absorption pathways of CSF obtained using Time-SLIP is that no flow or pulsation of the CSF is observed over the cerebral convexity (**Figure 7**). Even though strong CSF pulsation is observed from the prepontine and basilar cisterns to the Sylvian fissure, neither continuous flow nor pulsation of the CSF is observed from the Sylvian fissure to the cerebral fornix. The superficial Sylvian vein is present at this site, and the arachnoid membrane that covers it is strongly adherent to the vein. This indicates that the Sylvian fissure is practically at the distal end of the subarachnoid space. Although CSF is present on the brain surface, the Sylvian fissure poses considerable resistance to the flow of CSF. Accordingly, the absorption pathway of CSF is thought to exist somewhere proximal to the Sylvian fissure. As mentioned above, the most likely candidate is the route by which macromolecules in the CSF are absorbed into the lymphatic system from areas surrounding each of the cranial nerves or spinal nerves.

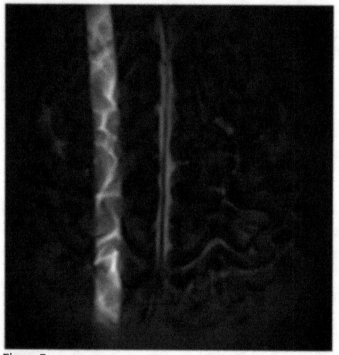

Figure 7

Axial view of the cerebral convexity in a normal volunteer. No cerebrospinal fluid (CSF) motion or flow is observed over the cerebral convexity. Supplementary video 7.

Go to:

CSF motion in the spinal subarachnoid space

When the flow of CSF in the subarachnoid space of the spine is visualized, the CSF is seen to pulsate along the ventral side of the spine in the supine position, but hardly any CSF flow is seen along the dorsal side of the spine. However, the CSF begins to pulsate along the dorsal side of the spine when the same examinee is placed in the prone position (10). On the basis of this finding as well, it appears that the CSF simply starts to move toward the location where it can flow more easily with little resistance (10). This observation differs considerably from the standard textbook description, which states that the CSF flows downward on the dorsal side of the spine and upward on the ventral side of the spine.

The spinal subarachnoid space is a cylindrical structure with its tip at the caudal end and it does not contain any internal partitions. It is very difficult to imagine that CSF flows in opposite directions on the dorsal side and ventral side. The observations underlying this theory of CSF flow in the subarachnoid space were reported by Di Chiro (48), who surgically removed the vertebral arches of an animal in the prone position and injected dye into the ventricles. Since the dye was seen to move downward in the spinal subarachnoid space, he concluded that the CSF flows downward on the dorsal side of the spine. In addition, since radioisotope injected into the lumbar subarachnoid space enters the cranium in humans (12), it was assumed that the CSF must flow upward on the ventral side of the spine because it flows downward on the dorsal side. Now that Time-SLIP has provided new information on CSF dynamics (10,11), it is clear that this assumption was a complete misinterpretation based on an experiment using an exogenous tracer. However, it has been accepted as the truth in CSF physiology for many years, and even today.

Go to:

Does the CSF circulate?

CSF pulsation observed by Time-SLIP was traced using semi-automated tracing software called Dynatracer (49). The movement of the tagged CSF can be traced over an observation time of 5 seconds. In **Figures 8** to to10,

10, the x-axis of the graphs represents the time after tagging and the y-axis represents the distance of CSF movement. The open circles and open squares on the graphs indicate the upper and lower positions of the tagged CSF over time. The open triangles indicate the average of the upper and lower points. These points tend to spread out over the time, but no unidirectional CSF flow was observed in the prepontine cistern (**Figure 8**) or in the spinal subarachnoid space (**Figure 9**). The CSF was found to exhibit pulsatile movement, but no bulk flow. These results suggest that there is no CSF circulation (bulk flow) as seen in the blood. In other words, CSF does not flow from the site of production to the site of absorption (**Figure 10**). This finding of a lack of CSF circulation does not conflict with the CSF theory recently proposed by Klarica and Oreskovic (50,51). In their theory, the cerebral blood vessels are responsible for CSF (water) transport, so there should be no CSF bulk flow from the choroid plexus in the lateral ventricles to the arachnoid villi on the cerebral convexity (8,9,52).

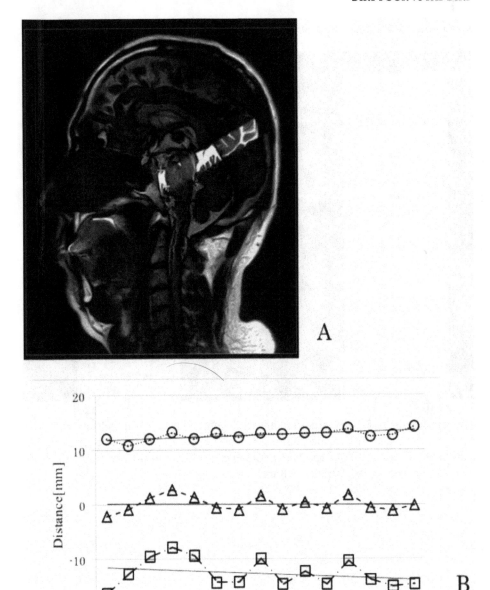

Figure 8

Cerebrospinal fluid (CSF) motion in the prepontine cistern was traced using semi-automated tracing software (Dynatracer) in the normal brain. The open circles and open squares indicate the upper and lower positions of the tagged CSF. The open triangles indicate the average of the upper and lower points. The tagged CSF had spread out by the time of observation. However, no unidirectional bulk CSF flow was observed.

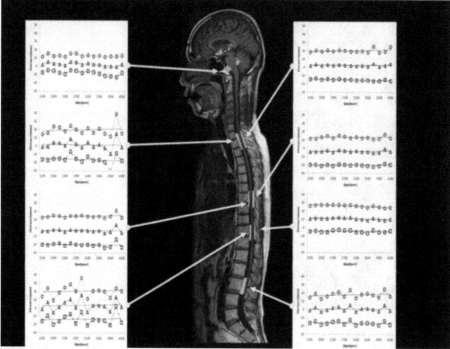

Figure 10

Midsagittal view of the entire brain and spine showing labeled cerebrospinal fluid (CSF) motion at different locations in the subarachnoid space as well as in the ventricles. The labeled CSF tended to spread over time, but no unidirectional bulk CSF flow was observed. Supplementary video 8.

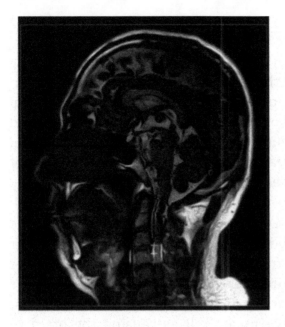

A

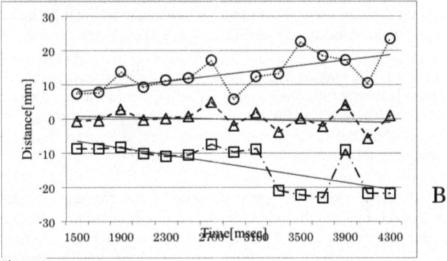

B

Figure 9

Cerebrospinal fluid (CSF) motion in the spinal subarachnoid space was traced using semi-automated tracing software (Dynatracer) in a normal volunteer. The open circles and open squares indicate the upper and lower positions of the tagged CSF. The open triangles indicate the average of the upper and lower points. The tagged CSF had spread out by the time of observation. However, no unidirectional bulk CSF flow was observed.

Go to:

Conclusion

It can be said that research on CSF dynamics has advanced to the next stage with the use of the innovative imaging method known as Time-SLIP. Obtaining a more accurate understanding of normal CSF physiology and pathophysiology should lead to improved diagnostic accuracy, permit the identification of new etiological factors in a variety of diseases, and promote the development of new therapeutic approaches.

The Carb Max Number in the Divine Mathematics Book & the AlgaRhythm Book should definitely be applied to children! Sugar not only limits the brain from fully developing, but also rewires the brain and can cross wire male/female hormones in children's brains. There is a wide variety of scientific journal literature on Sugar inhibiting Neurogenesis as well as causing the brain to shrink. Keep in mind we discussed Gaba & Amylin in regards to helping Insulin, they also build up when sugar and insulin build up. Amyloid Plaques are a leading cause of Alzheimer's Disease.

I am hopefully making a point here, your child's learning potential is based on how fully their brain can develop before about 7 years old, from there it's about training what they have to recognize patterns via the Language Acquisition Device that we actually detail very well in Melanin vs Diabetes book one.

The development of the brain, is what allows the areas of the brain to co-operate the key to Genius! These is based on having a strong toroid, vortex of clear phosphorus and iron rich CSF! That gamma wave activity, combined with a high powered vortex, is the hissing of God... the brain activity of Genius!

Lastly... The Carbohydrate that is hidden in the meat causing all kinds of trouble LOL...

Now in my opinion this is very much like the cancer causing

heterocyclic aromatic amines (HCAs) and polycyclic aromatic hydrocarbons (PAHs) of high temperature cooked flesh and oils like burned BATANA OIL, it is a sign that we should not be consuming these things, at least not as staple foods.

Mammalian meat allergy, alpha-gal allergy, red meat allergy, and lone-star tick bite meat allergy all come from a sugar in mammals (except humans and primates), Alpha Gal is the name. Hive like rashes, the feeling like you want to vomit and/or diarrhea. Symptoms can begin three to six hours after eating, some people may go into anaphylactic reactions that require medical attention immediately. The craziest part is that this reaction my not happen at all until you have the next helping of this meat. Get it.

Your in your yard having a cook out, eating barbecue, a tick bites you, you get a little itchy but no big deal. Two weeks later you have that same rib, pork or beef or whatever and BAMMM!!!! YOU HAVE A ALLERGIC REACTION TO A MEAT THAT YOU HAVE EATEN YOUR WHOLE LIFE! This is a new thing as per 2010 so if your Doctor graduated before then..... They may not be hip, you have to discuss these possibilities with your Doctor, if you or your child is having a allergic challenge.

BE MINDFUL ANTIHISTAMINES ARE KNOWN TO CONTRIBUTE TO SEIZURES, FLO JO THE FASTEST WOMAN KNOWN TO MAN, DIED OF A SEIZURE AFTER TAKE ANTIHISTAMINES (MAYBE UNRELATED BUT BECAREFUL AND FOLLOW THE GUIDANCE OF YOUR DOCTOR DON'T DIY)!

In fact lets close on some cheat codes:

Magnesium/Zinc - Inhibit Histamine Production and Release

*Water - Natural Anti-Histamine

Quercitin - Boosts Water's Anti-Histamine Ability

Vit C, B6 & Copper - Are Co-Factors for Diamine Oxidase
(DAO the enzyme that breaks down Histamine)

Selenium - Deficiency in most Asthma cases

EFAs Omega 3/6 - Regulate the body's inflammatory system

Gold - Reduces WBC count & activity (awesome against
inflammation & all Auto-Immune conditions)

Boron - Parasite

Note: Magnesium Deficiency boost Histadine Decarboxylase which
is the enzyme that converts histamine into histamine!!!!

Sidebar: DAO also breaks down Glutamate which is crucial
for gluten sensitivity, leaky gut syndrome, ADD/ADHD,
Anxiety, Seizures, MSG sensitivity and moor...

Printed in the USA
CPSIA information can be obtained
at www.ICGtesting.com
CBHW060322141124
17394CB00009B/129